Disaster Recovery Planning
for Telecommunications

For a complete list of *The Artech House Telecommunications Libra* turn to the back of this book. . .

Disaster Recovery Planning for Telecommunications

Leo A. Wrobel

Artech House
Boston • London

Library of Congress Cataloging-in-Publication Data

Wrobel, Leo A. (Leo Anthony)
    Disaster recovery planning for telecommunications / Leo A. Wrobel.
        p. cm.
    Includes bibliographical references.
    ISBN 0-89006-460-1
    1. Telecommunication systems--Security measures--Planning.
   2. Disaster relief--Planning. I. Title.
    TK5102.5.W76   1990   90-38012
    384--dc20   CIP

British Library Cataloguing in Publication Data

Wrobel, Leo A. (Leo Anthony)
    Disaster recovery planning for telecommunications.
    1. United States. Telecommunication services. Crises.
    Management
    I. Title
    384.06873

    ISBN 0-89006-460-1

© 1990 ARTECH HOUSE, Inc.

685 Canton Street
Norwood, MA 02062

International Standard Book Number: 0-89006-460-1
Library of Congress Catalog Card Number: 90-38012

10   9   8   7   6   5   4   3   2

Contents

Preface

When planning for any type of disaster, the natural tendency is to prepare for a worst-case scenario. This holds true in data processing disaster recovery as much as any other area of contingency planning.

A rational assumption is that if a company plans for the total loss of a computer or telemarketing center (due to fire, tornado, or whatever), a properly designed recovery plan should be able to address a disaster of a lesser scale. This is probably true, but let us ask ourselves two questions:

- Is a total loss of a data center really the worst-case scenario?
- Is it really the *worst* thing that could happen?

Consider the following scenario. Imagine that a data center is devastated by a tornado that occurs at 3 PM on a Thursday afternoon, injuring or killing two-thirds of the company's technical service staff. This would be far more severe in its consequences than one that occurred at 3 AM Sunday morning, because the latter at least would not affect the staff needed by the company to recover. Thus, the severity of a disaster must be gauged in large part by the resources that a company still has at its disposal to devote to recovery after the calamity.

Given this criterion, which disasters are the most destructive to the company and pose the greatest obstacles to recovery? Undoubtedly, disasters that leave the company impotent to recover after the disaster or those that cause it to rely heavily on outside sources for its recovery pose the severest threat.

We maintain that the most significant of these are major telecommunication disasters. These may not only put companies out of business, but may also render them incapable of helping themselves because such events are totally out of their control.

Examples abound. On May 8, 1988, fire destroyed Illinois Bell's Hinsdale switching office in western Chicago. Backup facilities were available for only 25% of the normal switched traffic load. As a result, some 50,000 serving links were affected for periods of two to ten weeks. Ironically, private line circuits, such as those used by reservations agents and telemarketing companies and other high volume users were generally the last to be restored. However, the disaster affected not only large companies. Dozens of small florists lost telephone service on their busiest day of the year, Mother's Day, and for several weeks after.

On February 18, 1987, fire damaged New York Telephone's Brunswick switching office in suburban New York. Service was out for up to a month. Imagine the consequences if the disaster had been only a few minutes away in New York's financial district. This was the New York metropolitan area's second major fire since 1975.

On February 25, 1987, the main AT&T switching computer failed in Dallas, Texas, isolating the 214 area code for most of a business day. While considered a "major outage," it was not as catastrophic as the Hinsdale and Brunswick events. However, many companies simply had to lose one-twentieth of a month's business if their business (airlines, for instance) depended on the phone.

The foregoing are but a few examples of disasters in which most companies had only one choice for recovery—sit back and wait!

Telecommunication disasters are also more insidious in their consequences than disasters confined to a single company. Like widespread natural disasters, hundreds of companies may be affected. With the possible exception of government and essential services, no one has priority in recovery operations.

From a broader perspective, consider the monumental changes in the U.S. telecommunication infrastructure since January 1984, when AT&T's monopoly was broken up. As has been the case in most areas of telecommunication, network disaster recovery has also become more complicated. No longer is there a single nationwide company with the ability to divert resources at will to a disaster area. To be sure, many managers within the Regional Bell Operating Companies (RBOCs) and AT&T still have their roots in the "Old Bell System" and cooperate with each other when disaster hits, but what will happen ten years from now when, through attrition, this comradery will have dissolved and these companies actually become competitors?

These changes and other events should cause all firms, telephone companies (telcos), and end-users alike to reconsider their options if a communication disaster were to befall them.

On the positive side, however, there are numerous options available for network disaster recovery that were unimaginable prior to 1984. Users now choose from myriad vendors offering switched T1 on demand, satellite access, intelligent switching and multiplexing equipment, and even redundant central offices. Commercial computer recovery centers have also honed their communication recovery capabilities to reflect a level of sophistication not thought possible a few years ago.

By developing an understanding of the inherent vulnerability in the network, users could best select from these alternatives, and protect their interests were the unthinkable to happen. This book is designed to provide that understanding.

Chapter 1
An Overview of the Public Network

1.1 UNDERSTANDING THE SCOPE OF THE TASK

The best start toward a reliable analysis of the risks in any network configuration is a general understanding of the topology of the public network.
Because disaster recovery planning (of which network disaster recovery
planning is a part) often falls under the auspices of a person with little
actual telecommunication experience, we will start with the basics.

This chapter provides a brief overview of a few typical configurations
used by business and industry to provide various switched and private line
(special circuit) services to end-users. Seasoned telecommunication professionals may want to skip over this first section, although it might be a
helpful refresher. In any case, referring to the figures should help illustrate
the task and foster a better understanding between the telecommunication
department and others involved in the overall plan.

1.2 GENERAL TOPOLOGY OF THE SWITCHED NETWORK

The lowly telephone is an easy instrument to take for granted. This is due
in large part to the fact that no matter how much people malign the
telephone company, the telephone works just as it is advertised, 99.999%
of the time. (How many other products can make that claim?)

At the touch of a button, a user can be connected within seconds to
any one of more than 300 million other subscribers nationwide. The telephone has become an integral part of our lives, our business, and our
economy. The communication infrastructure of the United States is un-
deniably the best in the world and is one of our most important national

assets. The telephone comprises one of the single most important basic components of our information economy.

Consider just a few of the developments in the last five years. On-line banking through expansion of automated teller machines and branches, and on-line credit verification (the little gizmo they run your credit card through before making a purchase) are two common examples. Some gas pumps now read your credit card, make an on-line transaction, and turn themselves on without human intervention. Burglar alarms automatically call fire or police. Portable on-line medical equipment monitors a patient's condition remotely and transmits it to physicians who may be hundreds of miles away.

New words, such as "telecommuter" and "telemarketer," have even appeared in our language over the last few years. The United States is indeed a different place because of the ability, in one form or another, to pick up the phone and call. Still, even given these developments and services, the basic telephone system is largely unchanged from 75 to 100 years ago. Many outlying areas still utilize step-by-step switching equipment originally developed in the 1890s! In the switched services arena, the basic framework and central office hierarchy is still much the same.

1.3 HISTORICAL OVERVIEW OF THE SWITCHING HIERARCHY

Prior to January 1, 1984, most switched traffic was carried solely by AT&T. Over the years a hierarchy for switching calls developed, much of which still survives today (see Fig. 1). Starting at the bottom of the figure (which could be better represented by a pyramid), we will briefly discuss each type, or "class," of serving office under the old Bell system. It may help to follow along in the figure.

Under the old switching hierarchy, all calls originated and terminated in a class 5 switch, shown at the bottom of Fig. 1. Offices of higher ranking (classes 4 through 1) handled toll traffic only. Calls progressed up the hierarchy, then across to the same or a lower-class office to the class 5 switch desired. The direct route to the next highest office in the priority scheme is called the *final* route. Lower-class offices switch to, or "home," to the office to which its final route is connected.

In addition to these final routes, direct trunk routes are also established between offices where there is a high volume of traffic. The switches will try to use these trunks first, but will route traffic up the hierarchy if none are available. Occasionally, modifications on this design did occur. Special circumstances often required a class 4 office to home on a class 2

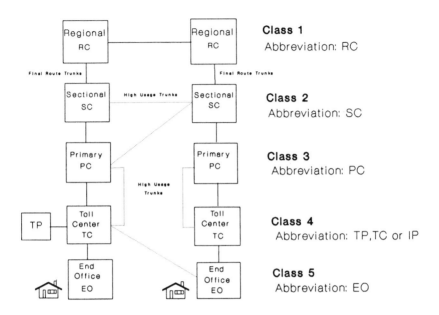

Figure 1 Telephone switching hierarchy prior to 1984.

or class 1, or a class 3 to home on a class 1, *et cetera*. In general, however, offices followed the hierarchy shown.

As can be seen in the figure, when a call originated in the "end office" (also known as the local serving office) that was destined for a subscriber in a different serving office, it was switched or "homed" to a toll center. From the toll center the call was switched to the desired class 5 end office, or if no trunks were installed or available, passed further up the hierarchy to a class 3 primary.

Once in the class 3 switch, the call would either utilize high usage trunks (if applicable) to another office or be routed via the final path to a sectional, or class 2, serving office. Sectional serving offices were usually the largest offices in a given metropolitan area and switched traffic from offices throughout the city.

The final stop in the old hierarchy was the regional or class 1 switching center. These offices were of supreme importance in the pre-1984 communication world. Numbering only seven nationwide, they each switched traffic for an area that consisted of five or more U.S. states and Canadian provinces.

1.4 OVERVIEW OF THE CURRENT SWITCHING HIERARCHY

Since 1984, the network has undergone many changes. At that time, AT&T negotiated a settlement to a long-running antitrust suit that dramatically changed the nature of how long-distance services are provided in the United States. While the fundamental hierarchy is much the same, major modifications had to be made to accommodate customer access to multiple carriers (see Fig. 2). This is known as "equal access."

The end office shown in the pre-1984 diagram is now referred to as an "Equal Access End Office," or EAEO. This designation denotes that the office has been modified or upgraded to allow access to multiple long-distance carriers. From an EAEO, a user accesses a presubscribed carrier simply by dialing 1 or 0 before making a call. A balloting process allows the end-user to choose a carrier. The end-user may also elect to access any *other* carrier serving his area by dialing the 10XXX code for that particular carrier. For example, if the user has selected MCI to be his 1 + (long-distance) carrier, but decides for whatever reason to use AT&T for a particular call, he can substitute the "1" with 10288-1 (the access code for AT&T) and complete the call on the AT&T network.

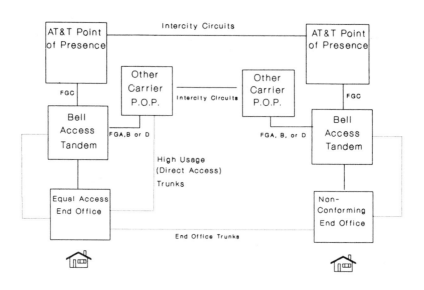

Figure 2 Telephone switching hierarchy after 1984.

Access codes for some of the major carriers are:

AT&T   10288
MCI   10222
Sprint   10333/10777
Metromedia   10084
ITT   10488
Claydesta   10987

These codes, incidentally, have a definite bearing on network disaster recovery. In the event of a major outage involving a long-haul carrier, a user in an EAEO has the option of simply dialing a five-digit code to bypass the crippled carrier company. For example, a customer who could not use AT&T during the January 15, 1990, network failure could have easily accessed another carrier by dialing the appropriate 10XXX code. Because AT&T was the only carrier affected, MCI, Sprint, and other carriers could still carry the call. The same would be true if an MCI user dialed the AT&T access code during an MCI failure.

A Non-Conforming End Office (NCEO), as shown in Fig. 2, is an office that houses an electromechanical or step-by-step switch that cannot be adapted easily for equal access. Therefore, these offices cannot support multiple carriers. Once upgraded, they become EAEOs, but until that time they default to AT&T for all traffic. In the interim, the only option at a customer's disposal for accessing other carriers from these offices is to dial either a 950-XXXX number or an 800 access number. This is similar to the access arrangement for other carriers that existed prior to the AT&T breakup, and still exists in many areas.

The second level of the post-1984 hierarchy is the "sector tandem." Sector tandems usually number only one per city and are not shown in Fig. 2.

The two most significant central offices in the post-divestiture environment are the end offices and the "access tandem" [see Fig. 3(a)]. Access tandems, or ATs, serve entire LATAs* and are of prime importance as they often serve as the gateway to many of the long-haul carriers serving the area. Access tandems most closely correspond with the sectional serving offices of the pre-divestiture era.

---

*A LATA, or Local Access Transport Area, is the geographic area in which the Bell Operating Company—not AT&T or other long-haul carrier—is the primary provider of long-distance service. Bell and other local companies like GTE, Centel, Contel, et cetera, provide connections "intra-LATA" or inside the LATA boundaries. AT&T and other long-haul carriers like MCI and Sprint provide "inter-LATA" service, or connections to other LATAs [see Fig. 3(b)].

Common Switching Office Classifications

Pre-Divestiture (Before 1984)			Post-Divestiture (After 1984)	
Class	Name	Abbreviation	Name	Abbreviation
1	Regional	RC	Point of Presence	POP
2	Sectional	SC	Access Tandem	AT
3	Primary	PC	Sector Tandem	ST
4C	Toll Center ∗	TC	Equal Access	
4P	Toll Point ∗	TP	End Office	EAEO
4X	Intermediate Point	IP	Non-Conforming	
5	End Office	EO	End Office	NCEO

∗ Toll Centers have operators,
Toll Points do not.

Figure 3(a) Common switching office classifications. (Courtesy of Premiere Network Services, Inc., Dallas, TX.)

Connections from long-distance carriers into and out of the local network are made through the AT or one of the EAEOs serving a given LATA. Generally speaking, traffic from low volume areas in the LATA is switched via common trunk groups between outlying offices and the AT. Traffic to long-distance carriers from high volume exchanges is switched via dedicated trunk groups between the carrier and a selected end office. Access via a 950-XXXX carrier, as explained later in this book, is provided almost exclusively from the AT.

1.5 PRIVATE LINE CIRCUIT TOPOLOGY

Typical private line circuits are the types of circuits that connect computers together or connect computers to remote terminals such as reservation centers, branch banks, *et cetera*. They are designed for very high volume users for which normal dial services would be too slow or too costly. AT&T, for example, offers more than 160 different types of private line services. (Private line or custom circuits are any kind of circuit other than simple telephone service.)

Private line circuits can be voice or data, analog or digital. Every private line circuit undergoes a custom engineering process in which facilities and equipment are specifically and meticulously selected to provide

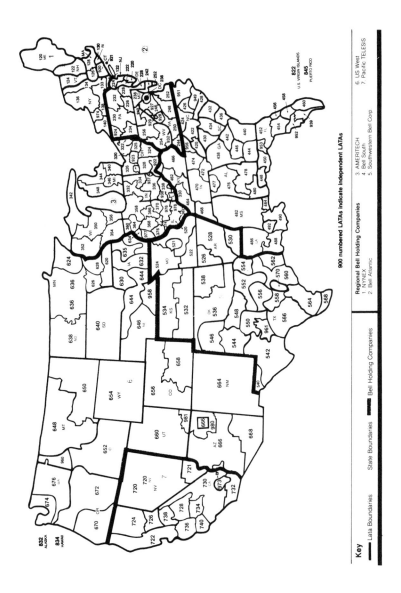

Figure 3(b) National LATA map. (Courtesy of CCMI/McGraw-Hill, reprinted with permission.)

the desired features and performance characteristics of the circuit. Voice circuits more than 1800 miles in length, for example, require echo suppression equipment. Data conditioning is required for some types of data, but not others, and where signaling is concerned, there are 100 different ways to ring a phone!

Each of the 160 classes of service in and of itself has dozens of potential "options" that can be selected to tailor the circuit to the exact needs of the user. Keep in mind, however, highly specialized circuits such as these often take months to design and install. This could mean considerable stumbling blocks in the disaster recovery process due to the specialization and inherent complexity of these circuits.

For purposes of an example, assume we have an analog data circuit that originates in a bank's computer room in Dallas and terminates in a branch office in New York. This is one of the most common types of data circuits in use today. You should look at Fig. 4 for clarification while we follow this hypothetical circuit.

Starting at the front-end processor, an RS232 connection is made into a private line modem. Four wires come out of the modem: two for a transmission path, two for a receiving path. These usually connect to four other wires (red, green, yellow, and black) provided by the telephone company on a network interface jack, punch-down block, or other "demark" point.

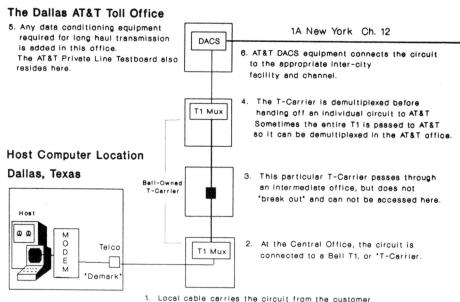

The Dallas AT&T Toll Office

5. Any data conditioning equipment required for long haul transmission is added in this office.
The AT&T Private Line Testboard also resides here.

1A New York Ch. 12

DACS

6. AT&T DACS equipment connects the circuit to the appropriate inter-city facility and channel.

T1 Mux

4. The T-Carrier is demultiplexed before handing off an individual circuit to AT&T Sometimes the entire T1 is passed to AT&T so it can be demultiplexed in the AT&T office.

Host Computer Location

Dallas, Texas

Bell-Owned T-Carrier

3. This particular T-Carrier passes through an intermediate office, but does not 'break out' and can not be accessed here.

Host

MODEM

Telco

'Demark'

T1 Mux

2. At the Central Office, the circuit is connected to a Bell T1, or 'T-Carrier.

1. Local cable carries the circuit from the customer location to the nearest Central Office.

Figure 4 Typical analog data circuit.

The telephone company's responsibilities begin at this interface. These wires terminate in the telephone company serving office that serves the user's area. They are rarely more than 18,000 cable feet in length due to line level loss. Thus, a typical local serving office covers a limited area, usually only a few miles across.

If we were to follow the four wires from the demark outward, the first major facility encountered would be the local serving office, or end office [see Fig. 5(a)]. The cable passes through equipment designed to protect the office from lightning before being routed to what is usually a T1 multiplexer, typically a D4 T1 channel bank. The telephone companies have employed T1 technologies internally since the 1960s. Virtually all interoffice communication today between Bell serving offices is on T1 (called "T Carrier" within the telco). For example, if you made a phone call across town this morning, you spoke over T1.

You should understand the T1 concept so that you can ask relevant questions and make informed decisions about T1 if it becomes necessary. For example, when we later address a "T1 conversion" for your company, you will realize that the actual technology employed is not changing at all. We will simply be moving the T1 out of a central telephone office to the customer location. Everything beyond this point stays the same, even after a user converts to T1 for local access.

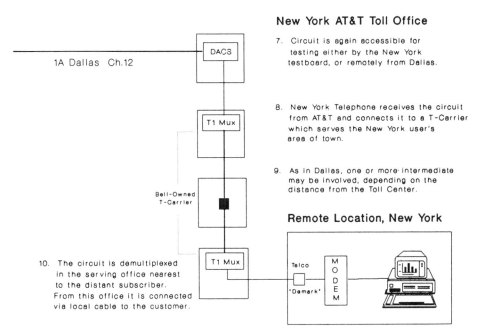

New York AT&T Toll Office

DACS

1A Dallas Ch.12

7. Circuit is again accessible for testing either by the New York testboard, or remotely from Dallas.

T1 Mux

8. New York Telephone receives the circuit from AT&T and connects it to a T-Carrier which serves the New York user's area of town.

9. As in Dallas, one or more intermediate may be involved, depending on the distance from the Toll Center.

Bell-Owned T-Carrier

Remote Location, New York

T1 Mux

Telco 'Demark'

MODEM

10. The circuit is demultiplexed in the serving office nearest to the distant subscriber. From this office it is connected via local cable to the customer.

Figure 5(a) The first stop for a company's intercity circuit is the local telephone office serving its area. A typical example is shown above. (Courtesy of Premiere Network Services, Inc., Dallas, TX.)

From the serving office, a circuit can be connected in a number of ways. If it is being connected to another user in the immediate area (in the same serving office), it may be simply tied back down to another local cable pair after some amplification. If it is going across town, it is connected to a T1 going to the serving office for that particular area and connected back again in that office to another four-wire access cable. Our hypothetical circuit, however, is going to New York, which means it must connect to a long-haul carrier.

Long-haul (intercity) carriers are served from regional offices called POPs (for "point of presence"), which serve as the "meeting place" where long-haul carriers connect to the local exchange carriers. The circuit is connected, via an interoffice T1 facility, to the Bell Regional Toll Office (BRTO). For private line "special circuits" such as this one, there are two types of regional serving offices of importance: the AT&T Toll Office and the BRTO as just mentioned. Because both evolved for the most part within the old Bell system, they are often collocated, many times residing together in the same building.

(1) The AT&T Toll Office or AT&T POP

All AT&T traffic for a given city routes through this facility [see Fig. 5(b)]. (In rare instances, there can be more than one per city.) It contains the regional switching center for all AT&T long-distance traffic, the private

Figure 5(b) The Dallas AT&T POP (background). In addition to providing the full comple-
ment of AT&T services to the Dallas LATA, this office also is a regional switching
center. Long-distance traffic for several states is switched here. (Courtesy of
Premiere Network Services, Inc., Dallas, TX.)

line (also called special service or custom service) testboard, the television
operations center (for network TV feeds), and sometimes even operator
service centers and other specialized functions.

(2) The Bell Regional Toll Office

This office, already of great importance in the pre-divestiture environment,
has now become even more so. It houses the equal access tandem switch,
which provides certain types of switched access services to all non-AT&T
carriers for the entire LATA. Either of these offices may also contain a
"digital hub," which controls all T1 and digital data service (DDS) for the
region. For our purposes we will assume that AT&T will be carrying this
circuit, so we should take a quick look inside the AT&T Toll Office before
we proceed.

   The regional toll centers are of supreme importance. Some of the
most critical components of the circuit are located here. This is the office
in which circuits are "bridged," that is, split out and fed to a number of
locations in a number of cities. The AT&T testboard, which the customer's
network control center calls in case of trouble, is usually located here.
Digital hubbing and specialized equalization or circuit conditioning equipment for the circuit may also be located here.

This circuit is but one of thousands of AT&T circuits or "serving links" for the entire region that pass through this facility. This in itself is quite remarkable from a management standpoint. Despite the difficulty of new circuit installations or maintenance, AT&T deserves credit for designing a system capable of maintaining more than 160 different classes of circuits on a scale of tens of thousands, while still keeping some semblance of order. Like any business faced with such a task, AT&T has been successful at this through heavy dependence on computerized databases.

1.6 CENTRAL OFFICE CROSS-CONNECTION METHODS

After accepting the circuit from the Bell company, it is connected through a distribution frame, in which wires are manually distributed within the central office, or a digital access cross-connect system (DACS) to the appropriate channel of the long-haul facility (see Fig. 6).

The traditional method of making central office cross-connection of circuit facilities, which involves soldering down wires on a distribution frame (labeled IDF in Fig. 6), is gradually being replaced by the DACS, which electronically connects circuits by means of a control terminal and specialized equipment.

AT&T has several types of long-haul facilities. They include coaxial cable, microwave radio, and fiber optic transmission mediums. Within AT&T, carriers are referred to as T carrier, N carrier, A carrier, L carrier, *et cetera,* depending on the type of facility used. An AT&T technician referring to a "1A New York channel 12" is talking about the carrier and channel on which a circuit is routed. This information is often useful if AT&T will provide it to you.

Channel 1 and channel 24 of a group, for example, are generally not assigned to high performance data traffic due to possible interference from other groups. If you hear a technician refer to your high performance data circuit as a "1A New York channel 24," red flags should go up. This rarely happens, however, because even if a circuit were to be engineered improperly, a technician would probably catch it later.

The circuit may route through several intermediate cities and "break out" (be accessible to test on an individual circuit level) on its way to New York. For example, rather than a direct Dallas to New York carrier, it may be assigned to a 12A Dallas–Columbus channel 11, then to a 3A Columbus–New York channel 16. This is generally done when a customer wants to "drop off" remote locations in Columbus.

Our example is a two-point circuit, so we will route it directly to New York for purposes of our discussion. The circuit will pass through

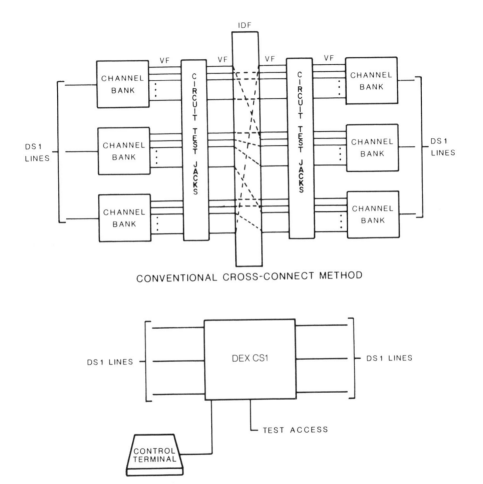

CONVENTIONAL CROSS-CONNECT METHOD

CROSS-CONNECT METHOD USING DEX CS1

Figure 6 Central office cross-connection methods. (Courtesy of DSC Communications Corporation, Plano, TX.)

numerous AT&T offices on the 1A New York channel 12 but will not break out until it hits New York. Once in New York, the first point encountered is an AT&T Regional Toll Office, the same type of facility as in Dallas. The circuit is again accessible for testing as it was in Dallas. Usually, however, New York will only perform tests if instructed by the Dallas testboard.

Because the main customer for the circuit resides in Dallas, the AT&T Dallas testboard is designated the Primary Control Office (PCO) for the circuit, which means the Dallas testboard directs all testing on this particular circuit. If the main customer were in New York, their roles would be reversed. This arrangement exists for a number of reasons, including administrative purposes and to avoid testing by two testboards on the same circuit at the same time, which might happen, for example, if users on both ends called in trouble simultaneously to their respective testboards.

Incidentally, the AT&T office in Dallas can actually test *inside* the New York toll office without the intervention of that office via a system called SARTS (Switched Access Remote Test System). AT&T offices routinely test in this fashion, calling on a technician in the distant office only if equipment must be changed or adjustments made.

After passing through the appropriate equipment in this serving office, the circuit is again connected to the Bell Operating Company, which in this case would be New York Telephone, via a DACS or distribution frame. While AT&T usually performs overall coordination (end-to-end service) on the circuit, it cannot get involved in maintenance or installation of either Bell circuit end facility. Its role is solely coordination and direction. The Bell company must do the actual work. Roughly stated, AT&T is Bell's customer and you are AT&T's customer.

After passing through the New York Telephone end office serving the area in which the New York user resides, it is assigned to a four-wire local access cable once again. This cable terminates in a 404B or comparable four-prong wall jack or something similar.

This is the demark for the far end. The telephone company and AT&T's responsibilities end here. From this jack, the wires connect to a modem as in Dallas. The output of the modem is the customer's communication controller, printer, or whatever the device is defined as in Dallas. Properly engineered and optioned, the output of the front-end processor in Dallas will match the output of the modem in New York exactly.

This scenario is replicated tens of thousands of times and for the most part works extremely well. The fact that overall availability of analog service within AT&T routinely exceeds 95% is quite remarkable, given the number of circuits, the huge number of circuit classes, and the number of things that can go wrong from point A to point B.

Chapter 2
Designing the Network to Survive

2.1 THE TYPICAL NETWORK

Unless you happen to be lucky enough to be designing a completely new network from scratch, you have probably inherited one that evolved based on speed—not efficiency.

Consider this common example. Installation of a circuit is most often a secondary concern at the time when most of the organization's energies are concentrated on opening a new branch, installing the new terminal equipment, picking out furniture, or whatever else is going on at a new location. Once a department gets around to notifying the telecommunication department, and once the telecommunication department finally gets around to placing an order with the telephone company, the requested installation date is invariably missed by two or three weeks. (Telecommunication departments are woefully out of touch with the overall corporate planning process in many cases.) A last-minute scramble ensues, calls are made, and after begging, pleading, and gnashing of teeth the circuit turns up more or less on time. (Please excuse the cynicism of a former telecommunication manager!)

The circuit is placed in service and with a sigh everyone moves on to the next crisis. After all, the circuit works, it is in the budget, and there are many other items to address. The problems are over, right? Wrong!

After this scenario is repeated several dozen times over the years, problems begin to develop for the disaster recovery planner. Dozens, sometimes hundreds, of individual circuits must now be restored should a disaster occur—a logistical nightmare to say the least. Large networks that develop in this manner are difficult to manage. For example, 100 individual circuits provide ample opportunity for problems with the network, which directly affects manpower costs for maintenance. This type of network is also costly and inefficient.

To complicate things further, true centralized control of the telecommunication function within most companies is rare. Oftentimes different departments or remote locations order services on their own, outside the corporate telecommunication umbrella. Even in companies where a strong corporate telecommunication department does exist, it must still cater to the unique needs of users. For example, when a development group announces that it needs asynchronous file transfers—even though the company has previously been committed to 100% SDLC (synchronous data link control)—the telecommunication department must usually accommodate the user.

Finally, network emphasis may vary even *within* a large corporate telecommunication department. A voice communication manager may view the switch as the center of the universe; the data communication manager may feel the same way about the front-end processor. Almost invariably, the two do not talk to one another. As a result, very complex networks evolve, all with different focal points, equipment, and responsible management.

To recap,

- The network is a dynamic, ever-changing environment. In most companies it includes many different technologies.
- It is often hastily designed and implemented.
- It is the responsibility of many different individuals, who often have different primary areas of interest.

The network contingency planner must unify this coalition and implement the grand strategy to assure continuity in network operation should disaster strike. A fine example of what is possible through use of a united planning effort can be found in Figs. 7(a,b). These two figures represent a cohesive methodology among departments that encompasses voice, data, and other diverse technologies.

One way to achieve this result is to unite all of the related departments behind a point of interest common to all. In many companies this common point, as evidenced in the figures, is the T1 transport network.

2.2 GOING T1—THE "WHYS"

Any company with a significant network size probably has T1 conversion plans on the table. Since 1984, the cost of T1 bandwidth has dropped dramatically. Notwithstanding the cost, however, a number of good rea-

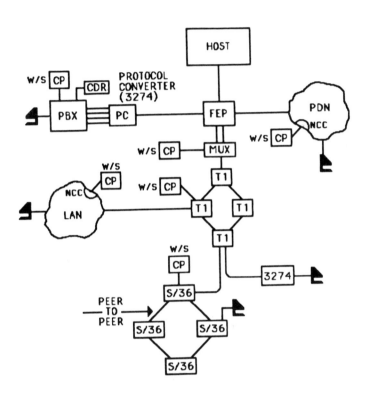

Figure 7(a) Complex connection. (Courtesy of D.M.W. Group, Ann Arbor, MI.)

sons exist for companies to begin using T1 technology, at least on the local access portion of the network.

In addition to generally improved circuit quality, there are four reasons to use T1:

1. Reduced cost;
2. Improved network management capability;
3. Preparation for upcoming new technologies, such as integrated services digital network (ISDN);
4. Improved network survivability and restoration.

We will consider each one at a time.

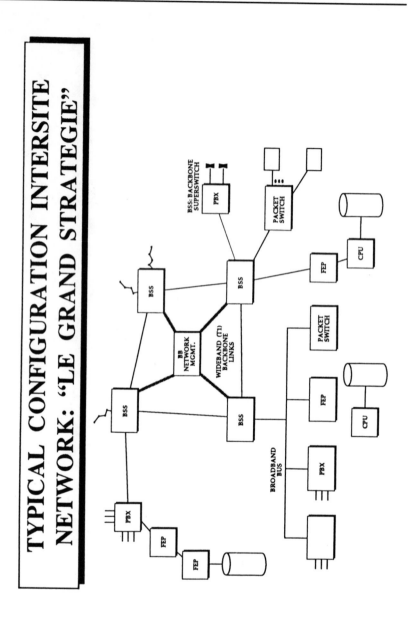

Figure 7(b) Le Grand Strategie. (Courtesy of D.M.W. Group, Ann Arbor, MI.)

(1) Reduced Cost

Table 1 contrasts the costs associated with individual voice-grade circuits compared to T1 local access, assuming a circuit length of about 10 mi. As can be seen from the table, the cost savings is on the order of 50 to 80%, depending on circuit type, with the breakpoint at 13 circuits. The breakpoint on digital circuits is even lower, perhaps as low as four, because of the high cost of digital local loops.

(2) Improved Network Management

T1 access configurations provide fewer possible failure points, thereby decreasing the amount of day-to-day troubleshooting. Additionally, since a few spare channels usually exist on the T1 access link to the carrier POP, the time required to install a new circuit is often shortened or at least simplified.

Finally, since T1 circuits are of such great importance, they are often given priority in major facility outages. Bell and AT&T restoration times on routine T1 outages are often less than the two-hour clearance on normal private line circuits. Thus, in a failure you lose more, but it is fixed faster. When you consider that any T1 access should utilize some kind of backup path determined by the user (as discussed later in this book) the availability of the link could approach 100%.

Table 1
The economics of T1 on local access

The following illustrates a circuit of approximately 10 miles (voice grade, 56 kb, and T1) under applicable Southwestern Bell tariffs.

Voice Grade	$109.74
56 kb	$344.92
T1	$823.10

To derive 24 voice-grade or 56 kb circuits from a T1, it is necessary to buy or lease multiplex equipment at each end. A ballpark figure for such equipment on a long-term lease might be $300 per month per end. Therefore, the following costs apply:

Cost of 24 voice-grade circuits = $109.74 × 24 = $2633.76
Cost of 24 56 kb circuits = $344.92 × 24 = $8278.08
Cost of 24 voice-grade or 56 kb circuits via T1 facility
= $823.10 + $300 + $300 = $1431.10/24 = $59.30

Therefore, the breakpoint in this case is 13 voice-grade or five 56 kb circuits.

(3) Preparation for New Technologies

ISDN is here today for many companies, with some 70,000 ISDN access lines installed throughout the United States as of December 1989. While many companies will not need ISDN capabilities for a number of years, the intermediate step of converting to digital transmission mediums (T1, 56 kb, *et cetera*) will ease the transition once the service becomes commonplace. T1 can be a beneficial training device for the staff that will help them become acquainted with the digital world. Regardless of the reasons, it would pay to become acquainted with these services because the most efficient network recovery assemblies are based on digital technologies.

(4) Greater Network Survivability

While cost and quality certainly are good considerations, one of the advantages that makes T1 attractive to the contingency planner is its ease of restoration. A single T1 circuit is much simpler to divert to a computer recovery facility, for instance, than 24 or more individual circuits. This ability to switch circuits in bulk, when combined with some thoughtful engineering on which circuits are assigned to which T1s, will simplify the recovery task (see Fig. 8). It is also much simpler to back up in the event of major local loop failures.

2.3 RULES FOR OPTIMIZING THE DESIGN

As mentioned at the beginning of this chapter, few of us involved in network contingency planning have the luxury of being able to start fresh with a clean slate on our network design. For most companies, the network is a dynamic, everchanging entity. So the whole plan must boil down to a series of cost trade-offs and a few simple rules.

You must be a creative thinker to be able to back up the network without necessarily *duplicating* the network (and the cost) in the process. To be cost effective, among other things a solution must:

1. *Keep reinstallation costs for new circuits at a minimum.* Any time new circuits must be installed, there are substantial up-front costs that must be considered. It is always wiser to try to utilize circuits already in service first.
2. *Utilize as much existing equipment as possible* to avoid buying new (such as modems, multiplexers, *et cetera*). This refers to equipment installed at remote locations. In addition to increased cost, stockpiling such things as dial-up modems for shipment to remote users

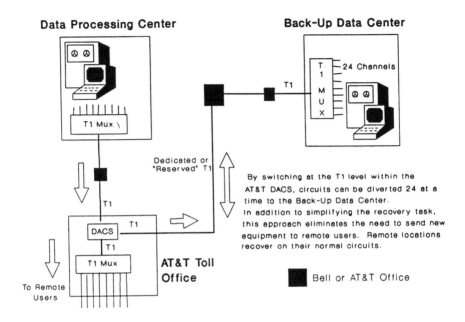

Figure 8 Efficient engineering of T1 local access to facilitate computer recovery.

in the event of a major disaster is a confusing solution. On the other hand, preinstalling backup equipment that is also used on a day-to-day basis is another situation altogether—it serves a dual purpose and is not a dead expense and is, therefore, a more acceptable solution.

3. *Avoid duplicating circuits* to the greatest extent possible (such as those installed passively to a recovery center that serve no other function). The safest approach to network recovery is to install one spare circuit to the recovery center for each circuit in day-to-day use, which also happens to be the most expensive solution by far. There are methodologies for achieving the same result, at far less expense, and they, again, involve using the existing network first. Add to it only when absolutely necessary.

4. *Utilize shared resources whenever possible.* This includes everything from reserved communication facilities to computer hot sites. Invariably, the cost of these services will be lower since it is spread

across a wide user base. This is especially true for such capital-intensive items as computer backup facilities.

5. *Utilize easily replaceable technology.* Avoid one of a kind equipment, multiplexers, *et cetera* that could be difficult to locate and replace in a disaster.

6. *Make use of technology that will adapt to future technological changes.* If the company changes its network design two years down the road, some foresight now can eliminate having to redesign the network recovery project at that time. Use technologies that will grow and adapt with your company.

7. *Conform to recognized industry standards.* Equipment that conforms to recognized standards is easier to replace in an emergency. It also helps minimize dependence on one single circuit or equipment vendor. Besides the obvious reasons for this rule, always remember that vendors can have disasters too.

8. *Be sure the plan can be tested easily with minimal service disruption.* Some network backup configurations can be designed for testing during normal business hours, eliminating the need for employees to come in on a weekend.

9. *Allow for less-than-total disaster response.* Many companies in the past have had to activate expensive computer recovery centers because of telecommunication disasters or other events unrelated to computer problems. The plan should be flexible enough to be able to address and respond selectively to disasters that are less than total in nature.

10. *Protect against day-to-day circuit disruptions.* The most common and aggravating problems are those of a day-to-day nature. Any systems that can be designed into the recovery planning effort that reduce daily circuit outages in addition to providing backup for catastrophic situations pay obvious dividends.

11. *Guard against common failure points, such as a single central office (CO).* This ties in with item 10, but addresses the issue on a broader plane, i.e., what happens when a major public communication company fails?

Chapter 3
Computer Disaster Recovery

3.1 AN OVERVIEW

American business is extraordinarily dependent on electronic data processing, and the need to protect these services has been around as long as data processing itself. This is why most large businesses have some kind of computer disaster recovery plan.

In a financially dependent service environment, business interruption insurance is no longer enough. An outage of as little as a few days can irreparably damage a company's image, and possibly spell the end for a corporation. If, for instance, you could not make a withdrawal on your checking or savings account for three days, what would your first course of action be when the computer came up on day four? If you are like most people, you would close your account and find another bank! Examiners know this, shareholders know this, and the federal government knows this, and that is exactly why banks are mandated to have recovery plans and why most other companies should.

The responsibility of the information services professional is to ensure that an unforeseen disaster never damages the integrity of the company. In today's "information age," when the fate of a corporation may be measured in hours, that has never been more difficult.

One popular option has been the Computer Disaster Recovery Center, or "hot site." These centers provide stand-by mainframes that literally wait for a disaster to happen. Centers are available for IBM, UNISYS, DEC, Sperry, and others. (Selected disaster recovery companies are listed in Table 2.)

Also available are conditioned computer rooms called "warm sites" or "shell sites"—large empty rooms with suitable computer support sys-

Table 2
Selected Computer Recovery Companies

Comdisco Recovery Services Inc. 6400 Shafer Court Rosemont, IL 60018	(312)698-3000
Corporate Contingency Services M/S L 856 P.O. Box 805 New Hudson, MI 48165	(313)486-2411
Hotsite 1000 Warren Avenue Niles, OH 44446	(216)652-9624
Premiere Network Services, Inc. 17304 N. Preston Road, Suite 800 Dallas, TX 75252	(214)733-6870
Sungard Recovery Services 1285 Drummers Lane Wayne, PA 19087	(215)341-8722

tems into which new equipment can be moved quickly (see Fig. 9). Warm sites and shell sites come in both fixed and mobile varieties and are available from a variety of sources.

3.2 COMPUTER DISASTER RECOVERY—A BRIEF HISTORY

Computer disaster recovery centers began appearing in the United States around the mid to late 1970s. Since then the mainframe recovery industry has become quite well accepted and very sophisticated.

All but the very largest mainframes can now be backed up in a commercial center. Sophisticated new offerings such as on-line tape vaulting have also begun to appear. The mainframe recovery industry has matured and is continuing to evolve. Groups and businesses involved with contingency planning are listed in Table 3.

For a number of reasons, however, telecommunication has lagged behind in the area of contingency planning. The last few years have included two Chicago COs crippled by flood and fire and major fiber optic cable routes washed away by floods and mud slides. Add to these events the hundreds of disruptions yearly when wayward backhoe operators cut telephone company cables—the most frequent type of communication disaster.

Figure 9 Computer disaster recovery. Warm sites are designed to move computer equipment into quickly after a disaster. (Courtesy of Premiere Network Services, Inc., Dallas, TX.)

3.3 RECENT DISASTER DECLARATIONS

Computer disaster recovery centers have been activated more times for disasters involving *telecommunication* than for any other single cause of disaster. The causes have varied—from earthquakes to floods to man-made disasters.

(1) The Hinsdale Central Office Disaster

On May 8, 1988, a fire put the Hinsdale CO (in western Chicago) of the Illinois Bell Telephone Company out of service in what has been termed the worst telecommunication disaster in U.S. history. The fire damage took more than a month to rectify.

The fire generated a debate about the phone company's preparedness and response capabilities, as well as the company's possible liability for millions of dollars of business lost by Bell's customers during the outage. The Illinois Commerce Commission has released a report saying that other COs across the United States are at risk. The report recommends changes in the network architecture, power supply design, and cable management. Illinois Bell, meanwhile, has been discussing the Hinsdale disaster with representatives of the telephone industry through a number of one-day forums and seminars.

Table 3
Contingency Planning Groups
Association of Contingency Planners

National Headquarters Tom Doemland P.O. Box 73-149 Long Beach, CA 90801 (213)932-3891	Orange County Chapter Nelson Mathews 777 S. Main Street, Suite 57-247 Orange, CA 92668 (818)339-9011
St. Louis Chapter Richard Arnold *Disaster Recovery Journal* 2712 Meramar Drive St. Louis, MO 63129 (314)846-1001	Minnesota Chapter Bruce Farr Burlington Northern 176 E. Fifth Street St. Paul, MN 55101 (612)298-7141
North Texas Chapter Wilda Wolf P.O. Box 515638 Dallas, TX 75251 (214)934-4465	Los Angeles Chapter Deborah Wood City National Bank 400 North Roxbury Beverly Hills, CA 90210 (213)550-5773

Other contingency planning groups

Deware Valley Disaster Recovery Information Exchange Group Jack Bannon General Electric Corporation Building 205-1 P.O. Box 8511 (08002) Cherry Hill, NJ 08358 (609)486-6056	Disaster Avoidance and Recovery Information Group John Toigo P.O. Box 5214 Largo, FL 34294-5214
Connecticut Disaster Recovery Information Exchange Lewis Vasques Aetna Life & Casualty Company M/S C-12E 151 Farmington Avenue Hartford, CT 06156 (203)273-1187	Disaster Recovery Information Exchange Rod Cross Corporate Business Systems Inc. 3 Director Court, Suite 103 Woodbridge, Ontario, Canada L4L 4S5 (416)748-1191

(2) The Brunswick Central Office Disaster

In February 1987, fire damaged the Brunswick CO in New York, disrupting service for up to a month. A similar situation in a New York City CO occurred in 1975. The latter was restored in ten days, possibly due to better coordination in a pre-divestiture era.

(3) Flooding in Chicago

A major finance company had its computer room under two feet of water for more than 24 hours during record rainfall and flooding in Chicago in August 1987. During the calamity, the press reported carp and minnows swimming freely through the facility and lodging in computer cabinets.

The company successfully activated a disaster recovery center to bring operations back on line. Recovery was completed at a Chicago area hot site within 13 hours. The computer center was then decontaminated and reoutfitted within ten days. According to reports, at least one telephone CO was affected by the flood.

(4) The San Francisco Earthquake

At approximately 5 PM on October 18, 1989, an earthquake of 7.0 magnitude on the Richter scale struck the San Francisco area. As a result, a record number of computer disaster recovery centers were activated (see Fig. 10).

While most structures containing computer centers remained intact, lack of commercial power forced the activation and relocation of business to the computer recovery centers. Most stays were brief, with companies returning to their primary place of business after power was restored. One CO was affected, again due to lack of commercial power and failure of backup generators. Surprisingly, most communication systems held up remarkably well and performed throughout the disaster, although some blockage on long distance did occur.

(5) The January 1990 AT&T Network Failure

In the words of AT&T Chairman Robert Allen, the January 15, 1990, network failure was "the most far-reaching service disruption ever." A software flaw in the AT&T long-distance network spread nationwide and resulted in the blockage of some 50% of all AT&T switched traffic for a period of nine hours. Services affected included long distance, 800, and software-defined networks. Private line service was not affected. AT&T normally carries 110,000,000 calls per day.

The probable cause was a computer conflict in backup CCS7 trunks designed, ironically, to provide redundancy. The incident has prompted renewed calls for cooperative arrangements among the major long-distance carriers in the event of major disruptions. Also comments were made that during this disruption, AT&T operators did not inform callers of the five-

Figure 10 The 1989 San Francisco earthquake. Upheaval of the earth during an earthquake can wreak havoc on a buried telephone plant. Pacific Bell and other companies in areas prone to such events have redesigned critical routes to sustain such violent motion better. The results have been impressive. During the 1989 San Francisco earthquake, all major communication routes remained intact. (Photographs © 1989 *Disaster Recovery Journal,* St. Louis, MO, reprinted with permission).

digit 10XXX access codes for MCI, Sprint, or other carriers who could have completed their calls.

The following is the official report on the outage, "Technical Background on AT&T's Network Slowdown, January 15, 1990," provided courtesy of AT&T, released January 24, 1990, and reprinted with permission.

At approximately 2:30 p.m. EST on Monday, January 15, one of AT&T's 4ESS toll switching systems in New York City experienced a minor hardware problem which activated normal fault recovery routines within the switch. This required the switch to briefly suspend new call processing until it completed its fault recovery action—a four- to six-second procedure. Such a suspension is a typical maintenance procedure, and is normally invisible to the calling public.

As part of our network management procedures, messages were automatically sent to connecting 4ESS switches requesting that no new calls be sent to this New York switch during this routine recovery interval. The switches receiving this message made a notation in their programs to show that the New York switch was temporarily out of service.

When the New York switch in question was ready to resume call processing a few seconds later, it sent out call attempts (known as IAMs—Initial Address Messages) to its connecting switches. When these switches started seeing call attempts from New York, they started making adjustments to their programs to recognize that New York was once again up-and-running and therefore able to receive new calls.

A processor in the 4ESS switch which links that switch to the CCS7 network holds the status information mentioned above. When this processor (called a Direct Link Node, or DLN) in a connecting switch received the first call attempt (IAM) from the previously out-of-service New York switch, it initiated a process to update its status map. As a result of a software flaw, this DLN processor was left vulnerable to disruption for several seconds. During this vulnerable time, the receipt of two call attempts from the New York switch—within an interval of 1/100th of a second—caused some data to become damaged. The DLN processor was then taken out of service to be reinitialized.

Since the DLN processor is duplicated, its mate took over the traffic load. However, a second couplet of closely spaced new call messages from the New York 4ESS switch hit the mate processor during the vulnerable period, causing it to be removed from service and temporarily isolating the switch from the CCS7 signaling network. The effect cascaded through the network as DLN processors in other switches similarly went out of service. The unstable condition continued because of the random nature of the failures and the constant pressure of the traffic load in the network providing the call-message triggers.

The software flaw was inadvertently introduced into all the 4ESS switches in the AT&T network as part of a mid-December software update. The main purpose of this update was to correct a weakness in the software that could cause a few calls to be lost during the reestablishment of normal CCS7 signaling between two offices following the removal of signaling network management controls. While the update had been rigorously tested in laboratory environments before it was introduced, the unique combination of events that led to this problem couldn't be predicted.

To troubleshoot the problem, AT&T engineers first tried an array of standard procedures to reestablish the integrity of the signaling network. In the past, these have been more than adequate to regain call processing. In this case, they proved inadequate. So we knew very early on we had a problem we had never seen before.

At the same time, we were looking at the pattern of error messages and trying to understand what they were telling us about this condition. We have a technical support facility that deals with network problems, and they became involved immediately. Bell Labs people in Illinois, Ohio, and New Jersey joined in moments later. Since we didn't understand the mechanism we were dealing with, we had to infer what was happening by looking at the signaling messages that were being passed, as well as looking at individual switches. We were able to stabilize the network by temporarily suspending signaling traffic on our backup links, which helped cut the load of messages to the affected DLN processors. At 11:30 p.m. EST on Monday, we had the last link in the network cleared.

On Tuesday, we took the faulty program update out of the switches and temporarily switched back to the previous program. We then started examining the faulty program with a fine-toothed comb, found the suspicious software, took it into the laboratory, and we were able to reproduce the problem. We have since corrected the flaw, tested the change, and restored the backup signaling links.

We believe the software design, development, and testing processes we use are based on solid, quality foundations. All future releases of software will continue to be rigorously tested. We will use the experience we've gained through this problem to further improve our procedures.

It is important to note that Monday's calling volume was not unusual; in fact, it was less than a normal Monday, and the network handled normal loads on previous weekdays. Although nothing can be guaranteed 100% of the time, what happened Monday was a series of events that had never occurred before.

With ongoing improvements to our design and delivery processes, we will continue to drive the probability of this type of incident occurring towards zero.

3.4 OTHER ARTICLES ON DISASTER DECLARATIONS AND RELATED TOPICS

"A Phoenix Rises in Brooklyn"
New York Telephone Brunswick Central Office recovers with the help of its vendors.
Telephony, April 27, 1987, p. 40

"Disaster in Dallas"
AT&T Network outage isolates 214 area code.
Telecommunications, May 1987, p. 114

"Centrex to the Rescue"
Indiana Bell and Eli Lilly
Telephony, August 10, 1987, p. 38

"DP Sites Drip Dry in Chicago"
Heavy rains disrupt Chicago area data processing operations.
Computerworld, August 24, 1987, p. 1

"Disaster Plans: Added Complexity"
How Hinsdale CO fire and related incidents complicate recovery planning efforts.
Computer Decisions, February 1988, p. 18

"It Was a Dark and Rainy Night. . . ."
Computer center flood of Household Finance Company, Chicago.
Computerworld, February 28, 1988, p. 14

"Lessons to be Learned from the Illinois Bell Fire"
Business Insurance, March 27, 1988, p. 28

"Fire KOs Chicago Networks"
Illinois Bell fire coverage
Computerworld, May 16, 1988, p. 1

"Nightmare on Lincoln St."
Illinois Bell disaster.
Telephone Engineering and Management, June 15, 1988, p. 82

"Rash of Disasters Just Fine by Surging Comdisco Unit"
Expansion of services by major disaster recovery service provider.
Computerworld, August 22, 1988, p. 63

"Copper Cable Thefts Hit Dallas"
Southwestern Bell experiences theft of copper cables, often cut right off poles, which
disrupts customers.
American Metal Market, August 28, 1988, p. 2

"Will Your Data Center Survive the Next Disaster?"
California quake boosts sales of computer recovery services.
Business Week, November 13, 1989, p. 102

Chapter 4
Telecommunication Disaster Recovery

4.1 TELECOMMUNICATION: THE WEAKEST LINK IN THE RECOVERY PLAN

Most components of a successful computer disaster recovery plan are commercially available and competitively priced. Standby mainframe configurations are available in many major cities. Companies, for the most part, are already accustomed to storing backup tapes off site to protect critical records. Many go to great lengths to establish formal agreements with service providers and have well documented plans for recovery on the computer systems level.

Unfortunately, communication often takes a back seat in the recovery planning process. Many companies simply have no idea how dependent they have become on the telecommunication network for conducting day-to-day business. A dedicated private line network that could have been easily backed up to a recovery center with dial-up lines a few years ago may now have evolved into a system of dozens or hundreds of circuits, creating a huge recovery task. Private line circuits are not easily replaced. Reinstallation can take months if there is no preplanning. Still, options exist for fast network restoration for companies willing to preplan and prepare.

4.2 OVERVIEW OF COMMUNICATION RECOVERY OPTIONS

A number of options exist for support of computer recovery centers or for backup communications in the event of accidental disruptions. A few of them are described in this section.

(1) Dial Backup

Dial backup is an acceptable solution for small networks, but it becomes too cumbersome as the network grows. Basically, dial backup uses the public switched network to back up private line circuits in the event of a disaster.

One problem with this method is the sheer number of lines required to restore even a medium-sized network. To back up 30 private line circuits, 60 phone lines are often needed; one for a transmission path and one for a receiving path. Another 60 phone lines are needed at the far end, two in each remote location. At, say, 25 cents per minute average long-distance rates, this solution could get expensive. Finally, monitoring 60 phone lines, each with a tendency to drop the connection, creates a maintenance headache.

Still, some bright spots are emerging in this area. Hot sites are improving their ability to manage dial-up service better through the use of matrix switches and patching arrangements. V.32 modems are appearing as the standard for 9600 b/s dial-up communication. In addition to advanced error correction, these modems also need only one phone line at each end for 9600 b/s transmission. Some also provide proprietary modes that increase to 14.4 kb, 19.2 kb, and beyond. Manufacturers of V.32-compatible modems are listed in Table 4.

Many recovery companies also offer lease retainers on "modem pools," which can be tapped for use by a client during a disaster. Long-distance usage charges may even be covered by some companies' business interruption insurance. Dedicated company voice networks may also be utilized to carry data during a disaster.

Table 4
Manufacturers of dial-up V.32-compatible modems

AT&T
Hayes
US Robotics
Datarace
Multitech
Microcom
Telebit
UDS
Ven-Tel
CDS
Motorola
Fastcomm

Also, with the advent of digital technologies such as fiber optic and digital radio transmission, the quality of switched long-distance service itself is constantly improving. Nonetheless, while these items make dial-up service slightly more attractive, it is still quite clumsy when compared to other higher capacity digital offerings.

(2) Reserved T1 with Central Office Multiplexing

Perhaps the most cost-effective and useful services for the backup of a large network are the high bandwidth digital technologies. These are switched services utilizing T1 (1.544 MB) and switched 56 kb bandwidth. The most common offerings belong to AT&T and are marketed as AT&T Accunet Reserve 1.5 T1 Service™ and AT&T Switched 56KB Service.™ By employing the proper multiplexing configuration with these kinds of services, dozens of circuits can be quickly and cost effectively transported to a computer recovery center or other location should a disaster occur.

A typical configuration follows. The scenario begins in the company's AT&T serving office. The end-user leases a central office multiplexer, which is located inside the AT&T toll office. (AT&T markets theirs as M24/M44 type multiplexing.) See Fig. 11.

Circuits usually carried through the AT&T toll CO are then "bridged" into the multiplexer, which sits passively in its normal configuration and has no effect on the network. The output of this multiplexer is a T1 circuit into a "port" on AT&T's DACS, which then switches the 24-channel T1 circuit to a spare or "reserved" AT&T T1 circuit going to the desired city to a waiting computer recovery center or other facility (assuming the recovery center has an access link to the AT&T DACS in that city).

Once at the recovery center, the process is reversed. The individual circuits are broken back out for termination into a front-end processor by means of an M24-compatible mux at the computer recovery center.

Incidentally, multiplexers known as M44-type muxes are capable of carrying up to 44 channels on a single T1 by utilizing a technology called ADPCM multiplexing. The maximum speed, however, for a data circuit on an ADPCM link cannot exceed 4800 b/s.

(3) Advantages of M24-Type Multiplexing

This approach has several distinct strengths compared to dial backup:

- New equipment does not need to be shipped to remote users to facilitate recovery. Remote users recover on the same circuits, only

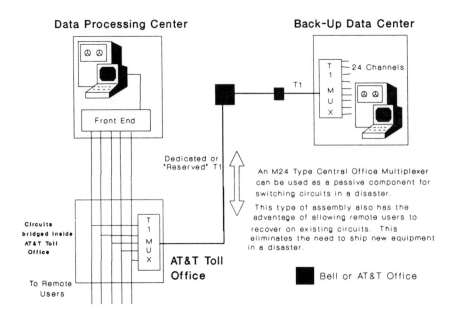

Figure 11 Central office M24-type multiplexing for facilitating network recovery.

now they are connected to the backup computer center via the reserved 1.5 T1 circuit instead of the original computer center. For example, no new modems or other equipment needs to be shipped out.

- Recovery is controlled by the host-site personnel. Dependence on nontechnical remote personnel is greatly reduced. Recovery solutions that depend on remote users are risky because communication with these persons would undoubtedly be impaired in an emergency. Your help number might not even work.
- The digital T1 medium is generally of much higher quality than dial-up circuits. Because digital circuits are regenerated periodically along the carrier route (as opposed to just being amplified like analog), they are of consistently higher quality.
- While usage charges for reserve 1.5 T1 can be as high as several hundred dollars per hour, it is still generally less expensive to utilize than dial backup lines. Monthly port and mux charges are usually in the $1000 to $1200 range per T1 switched. While usage charges can

be costly for extended tests, they may also be covered under business interruption insurance for actual disasters.

(4) Drawbacks to "Reserved" T1 Facilities

One major item to check, however, when choosing the T1 option is the availability of "reserved" facilities. Be sure the service provider (AT&T, Sprint, *et cetera*) has earmarked ample emergency bandwidth for use in case of a widespread disaster.

AT&T, for example, has limits on the amount of vacant T1s it can keep in its network because of the effects on its rate base. (AT&T is, after all, still a regulated carrier.) As a result, a widespread disaster could conceivably exhaust these facilities. T1s are dispensed on a first-come, first-served reservation basis, so many companies could be without T1 services in a widespread disaster, despite their "reservation."

You should also check the number of "ports" or access lines for reserve T1 service available into your company's primary computer recovery center. If there are none, they must be installed in advance. The cost to do so may be low because this item can be shared easily with other users of the recovery center.

Accunet Reserve is popular with many computer recovery centers because, like the recovery center itself, the Accunet access line can be spread over a large user base. Be advised that AT&T's Reserve 1.5 T1 Service can be preemptable or not. You should check with AT&T to determine which type of service your company has.

(5) Switched 56 kb Service

For companies requiring less than T1 bandwidth or those utilizing remote 56 kb hubs, switched 56 kb service may be in order (see Fig. 12). The same economic and quality advantages apply as with reserve T1 service. AT&T has long provided switched 56 kb service (see Tables 5 and 6). US Sprint also announced this service in Spring 1989. Other carriers, including some regional long-haul companies, are also beginning to offer it.

The economics of this service play out very nicely. When used, for instance, to restore 56 kb links to an IBM 3725/45 processor, dozens of terminals can be supported per 56 kb link. The service is almost as simple to use as making a regular long-distance call, and often costs about the same price. Sprint, for example, charges the same as its regular long-distance service for the ability to dial up a 56 kb path, although the user still needs some form of digital access line to utilize the service unless

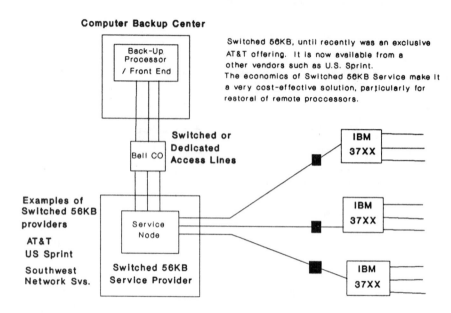

Figure 12 Switched 56 kb service for restoring remote processors from a computer backup site.

Table 5
AT&T's Switched 56KB Service rate schedule*

Mileage Band	Initial 30 s	Each Additional 6 s
0	0.156	0.011
1–10	0.156	0.011
11–22	0.156	0.011
23–55	0.169	0.014
26–124	0.169	0.016
125–292	0.169	0.019
293–430	0.169	0.021
431–925	0.181	0.024
926–1910	0.194	0.024
1911–3000	0.225	0.125
3000+	0.263	0.030

*As of January 1, 1990.

Table 6
AT&T Switched 56KB Service access cities

Akron, OH	Houston, TX	Philadelphia, PA
Albany, NY	Indianapolis, IN	Phoenix, AZ
Albuquerque, NM	Jackson, MS	Pittsburgh, PA
Anaheim, CA	Jacksonville, FL	Portland, Or
Atlanta, GA	Kansas City, KS	Reno, NV
Austin, TX	Knoxville, TN	Rochester, NY
Baltimore, MD	Lansing, MI	Sacramento, CA
Birmingham, AL	Little Rock, AR	Salt Lake City, UT
Boston, MA	Los Angeles, CA	San Antonio, TX
Buffalo, NY	Louisville, KY	San Diego, CA
Camden, NJ	Manchester, NH	San Francisco, CA
Charlotte, NC	Memphis, TN	San Jose, CA
Chicago, IL	Miami, FL	Seattle, WA
Cincinnati, OH	Milwaukee, WI	South Bend, IN
Cleveland, OH	Minneapolis, MN	Spokane, WA
Colorado Springs, CO	Mobile, AL	Springfield, MA
Columbia, SC	Nashville, TN	St. Louis, MO
Columbus, OH	New Haven, CT	Stockton, CA
Dallas, TX	New Orleans, LA	Syracuse, NY
Dayton, OH	New York, NY	Tampa, FL
Des Moines, IA	Newark, NJ	Toledo, OH
Detroit, MI	Norfolk, VA	Tulsa, OK
Grand Rapids, MI	Oakland, CA	Washington, DC
Greensboro, NC	Oklahoma City, OK	West Palm Beach, FL
Greenville, SC	Omaha, NE	White Plains, NY
Harrisburg, PA	Orlando, FL	Wichita, KS
Hartford, CT	Peoria, IL	

served in an area where the local operating company offers switched digital (measured) access lines.

Southwestern Bell Telephone recently filed a tariff to offer such a service to interexchange carriers. The trade name is Southwestern Bell Microlink I Access Capability.℠ While designed for interexchange carriers, it is also available to businesses within selected exchanges in Texas. The charge for the service (which is based on the Feature Group D rate plus a five-cent additive) is less than ten cents a minute.

Other operating companies either have or are planning comparable offerings. They make a very cost-effective enhancement to switched 56 kb service since the user pays only for actual use during testing or a disaster.

4.3 THE TELECOMMUNICATION RECOVERY CENTER

A relative newcomer in the field of disaster recovery is the Telecommunication Recovery Center (TRC). These centers are patterned somewhat after computer recovery centers. Some even include conditioned "shell site" space as a convenience to subscribers. The focus, however, is not on fast provision of mainframe capability as is the case with hot computer sites. As the name implies, a TRC provides protection of communication services. Only two dedicated telecommunication recovery companies currently exist (see Table 7), but others provide telecommunication backup services in addition to other services. Some specialize in microwave bypass connectivity. Others are common carriers that can be utilized to provide alternative serving offices. Lacking a provider of such services, oftentimes a customer will do the job itself. Consider the following example, we call it the "broom closet."

Table 7
Telecommunication recovery companies

Premiere Network Services, Inc.
17304 N. Preston Road, Suite 800
Dallas, TX 75252
(214)733-6870

Motorola Recovery Services*
20 Cabot Boulevard
Mansfield, MA 02048
(508)261-4200

*At publication time, Motorola announced that they were no longer formally offering network disaster recovery services. Motorola will continue to offer recovery-enhancing products that augment the service offerings of other providers and the needs of end-users.

4.4 THE "BROOM CLOSET"

In this scenario a company leases a small piece of real estate in a building near a Bell or AT&T toll office. The property is nothing fancy, in fact, something quite small but secure and out of the way (hence, the term *broom closet*). Private line circuit legs (spare master legs) are then positioned in the broom closet from the nearby Bell or AT&T office. A reserve T1 is also installed from the serving office to the broom closet.

The company then places a multiplexer in the broom closet and connects the circuits to it, and the output of the multiplexer to the T1 (see Fig. 13). Because the multiplexer may be any one that the customer chooses (as opposed to the standard D4 24-channel multiplexers that Bell or AT&T use), up to 128 circuits can be carried per T1, depending on the multiplex vendor. Make sure that the phone company installs redundant *master* legs, not just another remote circuit leg. Either through mistakes in ordering

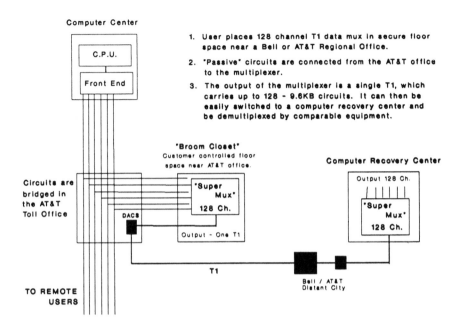

Computer Center

C.P.U.

Front End

1. User places 128 channel T1 data mux in secure floor space near a Bell or AT&T Regional Office.

2. "Passive" circuits are connected from the AT&T office to the multiplexer.

3. The output of the multiplexer is a single T1, which carries up to 128 - 9.6KB circuits. It can then be easily switched to a computer recovery center and be demultiplexed by comparable equipment.

"Broom Closet"
Customer controlled floor
space near AT&T office.

Computer Recovery Center

Output 128 Ch.

"Super Mux" 128 Ch.

Circuits are
bridged in
the AT&T
Toll Office

DACS

"Super Mux" 128 Ch.

Output - One T1

T1

Bell / AT&T
Distant City

TO REMOTE
USERS

Figure 13 The "broom closet" approach.

or processing, remote (rather than alternate master) legs are often installed. They are of no use in this application. These passive circuits also need to be tested regularly, at least monthly, to be sure that they are available when needed.

The advantages of this approach are the greater number of circuits possible per T1, as well as greater direct control of the recovery process by the company. There are also some obvious disadvantages. One is security; be sure the space selected locks and is not accessible to unauthorized personnel. The space should have a sufficient power supply and good air flow. Remember, this small room will become quite full of heat-producing equipment as the network grows, so plan accordingly.

These are minor considerations, however, since only passive (spare) circuits are used. In the worst-case scenario, the building burns and the company loses a multiplexer as well as its backup capability, but primary service stays intact.

There are scenarios like this one, however, that do involve primary communication. They most certainly should be considered, but remember that more rigorous precautions need to be taken if the solution involves your company's primary communication system. Also advantageous would be the use of a common carrier POP as the company's "broom closet."

4.5 EQUIPMENT COLLOCATION WITH COMMON CARRIERS

Some carrier companies will allow collocation of customer-owned equipment in their POPs. This can be a big advantage to the customer since the company can set up a "broom closet" with its carrier, thus avoiding access charges normally paid between the broom closet and another CO. Additionally, a good idea may be to consider carrier POPs for remote communication hubs (such as remote front-end processors and multiplexers) instead of remote branch offices owned by your company. In addition to the savings in access charges, there is a second good reason. Branch offices tend to close and move. Communications POPs tend to stay in one place. Finally, this approach allows the company collocating with the carrier to order from the carrier's choice of access or business office tariffs, whichever is most advantageous. Special offerings and feature group packages normally only available to carriers might also be available to the collocating company. Figure 14 illustrates an AT&T service node with T1 access.

4.6 ANALYSIS OF CARRIERS FOR EQUIPMENT COLLOCATION

The use of other common carriers (e.g., MCI, Sprint, Qwest) is becoming increasingly popular with companies seeking a backup to the AT&T Toll or Bell Regional Tandem, or a convenient place to collocate equipment. Many companies even place microwave links directly into these companies to gain the additional advantage of diversity on local loops, addressing the familiar problem of "backhoe fade." The days of total dependence on a single carrier appear to be over, with more users than ever insisting on two carriers and two diverse paths. This is not surprising considering that even COs have not proven to be 100% infallible.

Caution should be utilized when selecting a company for an alternative serving office. Take into consideration items such as the fact that many of these carriers pass through the Regional Bell Toll Office before connecting with their long-haul network. This negates any advantage if one of your requirements is to provide backup for the regional toll office! This would not matter if the carrier were simply being used as a "broom closet" for equipment, but it would spell trouble in the event that the regional toll office had a Hinsdale type of disaster.

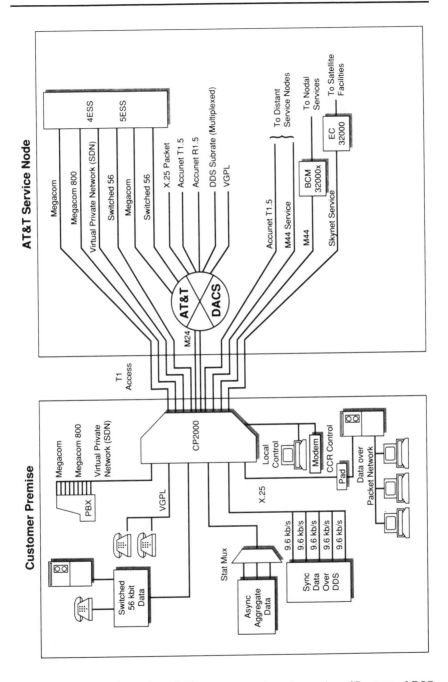

Figure 14 AT&T service node with T1 access on customer's premises. (Courtesy of DSC Communications Corporation, Plano, TX.)

A thorough analysis of the carrier company's circuit routing, access facilities, and physical security are a must before any decision is made. Some items to consider follow.

1. Does the proposed carrier's POP have clear line of sight to your company's location? Microwave, either on a full-time or emergency basis could be very valuable (as evidenced by its usefulness after the Hinsdale fire).
2. What kinds of businesses are in the building with the proposed carrier? Any company dealing with hazardous materials, *et cetera,* should be grounds for concern.
3. Is there adequate fire protection? Does the building or suite have Halon protection or sprinklers?
4. What kind of telcommunication cable facilities are in the building? Are they adequate in number? Are they shared with other tenants? Who else has access to the telephone room? How far is it to the Regional Bell Toll Office?
5. Is ample air conditioning and backup power available? If computer equipment is being located, is the commercial power clean and free of voltage spikes?
6. Is the POP manned 24 hours? If not, are there procedures for access after hours?
7. Will the carrier's on-site personnel provide "test assists" on equipment your company owns? For example, can your company's network control center ask one of the carrier company's technicians to help isolate equipment trouble, or will they have to dispatch their own technician? Does your company *want* the carrier company to touch its equipment? If not, can they prevent them?
8. Does your carrier's insurance cover your equipment, or is it necessary to take out a rider on your policy? If your equipment is leased, will the leasing company allow it to be installed off the premises of your main building?

In summary, carrier POPs can be excellent choices for placement of communication hubs or equipment. Be aware, however, that collocation is still relatively new and there are no "standards" on what to look and ask for other than good common sense. Still, with many long-haul carriers competing for new business, there are good deals to be had.

Chapter 5

Backup for Central Offices

5.1 USING CARRIER POPS FOR CENTRAL OFFICE DIVERSITY

Common carrier POPs can be used in disaster recovery applications as backup for a Bell Access Tandem or a critical EO. Before we begin, realize that there are no easy fixes for a CO disaster. There is only one kind of CO disaster—the messy kind. There are, however, steps that can be taken to mitigate the effects of a failure.

Figure 15 shows a diagram of the fictitious ABC Company with a communication hub in a common carrier's POP, as described in the last chapter. The hub is fed by Bell access lines as well as a microwave access link. There are two diverse paths on the local facilities and two diverse COs.

On a daily basis, the company is protected from local cable cuts through use of the microwave access link. There is also enough surplus capacity on the Bell T1 access circuits to move all critical traffic to these links in case the microwave system were to fail. AT&T Accunet Reserve links can also be in place to the POP to facilitate restoration in the event the ABC Company data center is forced to move to a disaster recovery center in another city.

Figure 15 also illustrates what happens in the event of a disaster at the local EO that serves the ABC Company. With the Bell T1s out of commission indefinitely, spare T1s are commandeered from the microwave system and reconnected in the common carrier POP. The T1 loops between the carrier POP and the Bell primary serving office are now useless, because they are part of the T1 circuits from the damaged CO. They are preempted and used to connect the new microwave T1s into the Bell primary CO, thereby restoring service.

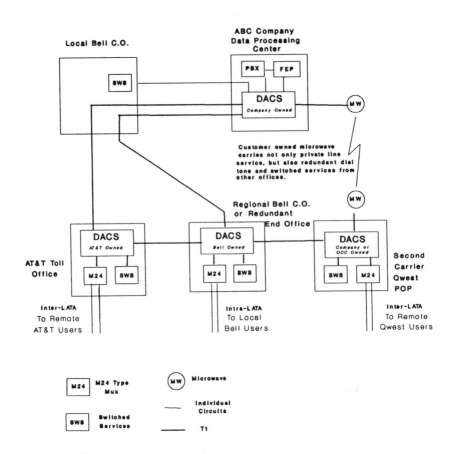

Figure 15 Using a common carrier POP for CO diversity.

These types of plans can and should be worked out in advance with the Bell company. In some cases, you could have your company's Bell account representative keep "standing orders in the pipe" should they ever experience this kind of disaster or get an emergency call from you for another reason. The local operating company should be an active participant in the company's recovery planning effort.

Consider, also, that in a disaster there is little chance that the Bell company is going to throw the doors of its central offices open for your technicians to make connections! Your company may be several days down the priority list for restoration. Even if facilities are available, you will probably have to wait for the phone company. So, if your company wants to maintain direct control of the recovery process, your plans should call for connections to be made within a common carrier POP, or remotely by dial-in reconfiguration methods.

When you consider the additional dimension added by use of Bell's dial-in customer-controlled DACS systems, the response is even better. Figure 16 shows how a network control center can make its own connections, without dependence on the Bell company, in the event of a disaster. This would be particularly important because, as we have said, there are no priorities in a disaster and the wait for service restoration could be a long one.

5.2 DISASTER IN THE BELL ACCESS TANDEM OR AT&T TOLL CENTER

What happens when a disaster takes place in the Bell Regional Toll Office or a critical EO? This scenario is not as farfetched as it sounds. Any place that counts on people in order to function has the potential for trouble, whether it is careless smokers, nonadherence to procedure, or deliberate sabotage. A day-long outage in the AT&T Framingham, MA, switch two years ago, for example, was caused by employees blowing two main fuses because they followed an improper procedure.

In addition to accidental disruption, both Bell and AT&T are susceptible to possible disruption every three years at labor contract negotiation time. Whether these disruptions are caused by labor unrest, or simply by individuals taking advantage of publicity, is not entirely clear. They do, however, happen.

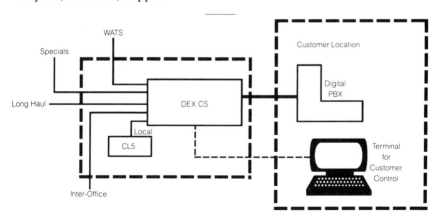

Figure 16 Customer-controlled network management. (Courtesy of DSC Communications Corporation, Plano, TX.)

In 1986, these disruptions included the deliberate sawing of a fiber optic cable (in a manner that made it difficult to repair) that blacked out a large part of the AT&T digital capacity to the U.S. West Coast. This event occurred during a strike.

In 1989, unruly picket lines were suspected of causing similar damage in New Jersey, again with severed fiber optic cables, during a New York Telephone strike. In these and other instances, fiber links were targeted due to their high capacity, high visibility, and difficulty to repair.

Before we continue, realize that we do not intend to offend AT&T, Bell, their unions, or the millions of dedicated workers within them. Their work over the years in responding during times of disaster outweighs these incidents a hundredfold. Contingency planning, however, involves planning for all contingencies, including (especially) those we often do not like to talk about. In this age of increased terrorism, when all public institutions are at risk, these subjects must be discussed and taken under advisement as a part of the contingency planning process.

5.3 CONSEQUENCES OF A TOLL CENTER DISASTER

In a worst-case scenario, a toll center disaster could affect the following, depending on the size of the city, number of COs, configuration of the metropolitan network, spare capacity available in the network, and other factors.

1. Inter-LATA switched toll traffic that utilized the access tandem in the Bell regional CO (perhaps 90% in some small- to medium-sized cities, less in the large metropolitan areas).
2. Intra-LATA and intercity traffic that switched through this CO (perhaps up to 50% of the intracity traffic, more than 90% of intra-LATA long distance).
3. Local service in this office's service office (100% assuming a total loss of the serving switch).
4. AT&T private line service (up to 100% in smaller cities with col-located Bell/AT&T POPs, less in larger metropolitan areas with separated POPs or multiple primary COs).
5. All digital service utilizing the DDS hub at the Bell regional CO (75% of all digital and T1).

Some items that *may* not be affected:

1. Cellular service (if it switches through another office and does not use the regional access tandem switch).
2. Intracity traffic that does not pass through the Bell Access Tandem switch (such as high usage trunks that connect many EOs directly to

one another). We assume that most long-distance traffic to outlying areas within the LATA *would* pass through this switch and thus would be out of service.

3. Other carrier companies (such as fiber carriers) but *only* if they do not utilize a high capacity hub within the affected Regional Access Tandem office (many might).

4. AT&T network television feeds. These could be largely unaffected since they often come in from local affiliates on microwave and leave on microwave or satellite (resulting in ample TV coverage of the disaster!).

5. Microwave common carriers but *only* if they leave town without connecting to a hub in the Bell primary CO.

6. Certain satellite carriers.

Many private line access links to carriers would presumably be down. Since many common carriers reside in the downtown area, they could be isolated by a disaster in the main downtown toll center. (The toll center might also provide local access services for these carriers.) Some carriers, however, pass through the Bell primary serving office even *before* getting to their long-haul network. So, effectively, a toll center failure would isolate these carriers from their long-haul network as well.

For example, consider the plight of a regional fiber-optic-based carrier that builds to the edge of a major city. Rather than buy expensive right of ways to the downtown area, they opt instead to simply lease DS-3 capacity from the Bell company. This DS-3 may pass through several Bell COs on its way to the carrier's POP, including the one devastated by the CO disaster. Carriers in this category would be down for the duration, unless temporary facilities could be set up. Many of these companies do purchase route diversity from Bell to preclude something like this from happening, and they also set up "fiber loops" for backup.

Microwave carriers may not be affected. Many leave downtown on their own radio systems, which are, of course, redundant from the local operating company. The same can be true of satellite carriers. Even so, it is wise to check before signing on with a common carrier, because either type of company—microwave or satellite—may also lease Bell fiber. For instance, a fiber link may be used to connect to a teleport up-link in an outlying location if coordination of frequencies happened to be a problem when the system was constructed.

5.4 THINKING THE UNTHINKABLE

Just how catastrophic a primary CO disaster would be is hard to gauge. Indeed, in most cases we have had to wait for CO disasters to happen to see exactly what is affected. It is almost like waiting for an earthquake. In fact, there are some parallels that can be drawn between an earthquake and a major telecommunication disaster.

The 1989 San Francisco Earthquake—The Big One?

In October 1989, San Francisco experienced a major earthquake—7.1 on the Richter scale. No one knew just how bad an earthquake of that magnitude would be. We just had to wait for it to happen. Well, it did happen, but, bad as it was, it was not "the big one" everyone was expecting.

The 1988 Hinsdale Fire—The Big One?

In May 1988, Chicago experienced a major communication disaster—the Hinsdale CO fire. More computer disaster recovery centers were activated on that day than for any other single event, including the 1989 San Francisco earthquake. The damage from the fire was pretty bad too. But it was not "the big one" of telecommunication disasters.

The unthinkable telecommunication disaster will be a disaster involving a Regional Bell or AT&T Toll Center. It may be next month, next year, or in 50 years. But as long as COs are critical hubs, they will continue to remain vulnerable as targets for terrorism, deranged minds, or accidental mishaps. The "big one" in communications, as in earthquakes, will be much worse than a 7.1; in fact, it could be an order of magnitude higher— worse by a factor of 10.

5.5 OPTIONS IN A REGIONAL CENTRAL OFFICE DISASTER

Some services are more resistant to disasters in regional COs or EOs.
- Microwave or digital radio common carriers
- Satellite common carriers
- Carriers that do not have a hub in the primary CO
- Selected cellular companies
- High frequency radio, tropospheric scatter systems (such as military, Department of Defense, *et cetera*).

The first two choices, microwave and satellite, are readily available in most major cities. The third, carriers that do not have a hub in the regional CO, may be difficult to find. (Check thoroughly; be sure the salesman *really* knows how the network is laid out.) The fourth, cellular, is currently useful only on a limited basis, but this is changing. The last choice is generally restricted, and not available unless you happen to be a telecommunication planner for the military or emergency government agency. For purposes of this discussion, we will concentrate on digital radio (microwave), satellite, and cellular.

Because microwave and satellite technologies can be inspected first hand to assure diversity from both major CO and major carrier (fiber optic and cable) routes, they are adaptable to a number of situations. The correct mix of these mediums in your network could prove most beneficial. A high capacity link to a satellite up-link or "teleport," which is normally used for video conferencing, can have great value in a major telecommunication disaster.

5.6 USE OF MICROWAVE FOR RECOVERY

Despite claims by some carriers about "all fiber optic" networks, most of the major carriers still utilize microwave and digital radio for a significant portion of the long-haul networks—and for good reason. Analog microwave technology has served the communication world admirably since the 1950s, and newer digital radio systems will undoubtedly carry us into the twenty-first century and beyond. When engineered and applied properly in the network, microwave is a proven and reliable technology with very positive effects on network integrity.

One common misconception among users is that in order for service to be "digital" it must be fiber optic. A tendency exists, particularly among less educated users, to equate "digital" and "fiber" as one in the same (due in large part to the marketing hype of recent years). True, fiber optics do use digital technology, but so does digital radio, and even T1 service, which uses primarily copper wire. Modern digital radio based carriers can equal or even surpass the overall performance and availability of fiber optic systems. When properly engineered and maintained, availability on the order of 99.98% or more is not only possible, but currently available in the industry.

If a microwave-based common carrier is to be used for primary circuit traffic in addition to disaster recovery, a number of questions must be asked.

1. What radio frequency is used for the majority of the network? A frequency of 2 to 6 GHz is much less susceptible to atmospheric interference than one above, say, 11 GHz.
2. Is the system truly digital, or does it employ "digital over voice" technologies (analog supergroups converted to digital)? True digital

performance is superior. Small and little known carriers are not the only ones to use digital over voice technologies; AT&T has utilized it for years, although it is being phased out.

3. What is the average path length of the system? (Path length is the distance between repeater towers.) Older analog radios often used path lengths of as much as 30 miles or more. While suitable for voice, the resulting signal fade and noise from these systems can alter data transmission. Since the received signal level drops dramatically as path lengths increase, the difference between a 25- and a 30-mile path is very substantial. Optimal path lengths for modern data transmission should be in the 22- to 25-mile range. Also ask if the carrier employs "space diversity." This involves placing antennas at slightly different elevations, allowing equipment to utilize automatically the one that has the strongest signal at a given instant in time.

4. Because no network is stronger than its weakest link, check for the presence of backup power generators at all repeater sites. Portable equipment serving several sites should not be acceptable since there could be problems moving it to where it is needed most, for instance, during hurricanes or other natural disasters. On-site backup generators supplying station batteries are a must.

5. As with any technology, there should be a method to guard against common equipment failure. Optimally this should be a "hitless switching" arrangement to change from a primary to a backup radio in the event of radio component failures. This feature is common among equipment manufacturers, but it is not always employed by the carriers themselves. This same equipment can be used, for example, to make additional channels available on a full system.

6. Finally, judge the microwave carrier using the same criteria as one would use to judge other carriers, such as technical support, trouble response, overall availability, and price.

Again, a properly engineered digital radio carrier can provide diversity around common COs or major fiber optic routes, and do so without degradation of service.

By combining microwave technology with some of the collocation and alternative access schemes described earlier in this book, an intercity link can be engineered that is 100% digital radio from end to end—never touching either a local CO or common carrier right of way. This can be of great benefit to the overall integrity of the network, while providing quality service to the end-user. Today, major digital radio carriers have formed consortiums that span the United States, and they offer services that are totally redundant of the major fiber optic routes. See Figs. 17, 18, and 19.

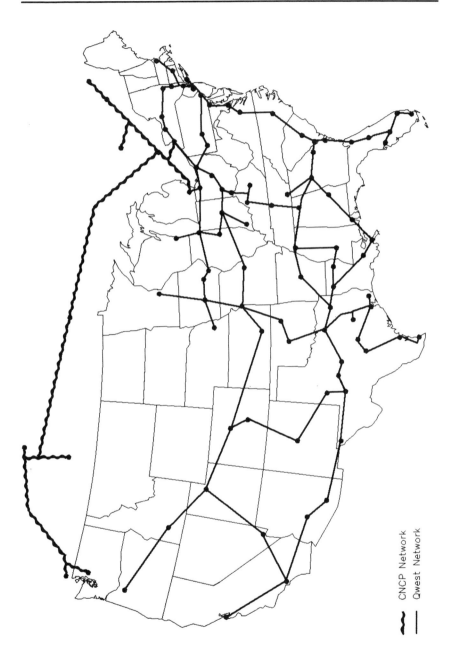

CNCP Network
Qwest Network

Figure 17 Major microwave carrier routes. (Courtesy of Qwest Microwave, Inc., Dallas, TX.)

Figure 18 AT&T microwave junction site, West, TX. (Courtesy of Premiere Network Services, Inc., Dallas, TX.)

5.7 USE OF SATELLITE FOR RECOVERY

Satellite transmission is another medium well suited to diverse end-to-end connections. It is finding increasing use both in primary circuit applications and disaster recovery.

Two types of satellite transmission are currently in use, they are "C" and "Ku" band satellite. They are conceptually similar, in a way, to the VHF and UHF bands on commercial television.

The C band has been around the longest and generally operates in the 6-GHz band. Since it has been in use longer, it is also the most difficult to license in congested urban areas. It also requires a very large antenna or "dish," which can be 12 to 30 feet in diameter. This can be a problem in areas of restricted zoning.

The Ku band operates in the 12- or 14-GHz range. As with microwave, its higher frequency is more easily attenuated by atmospheric conditions. It can operate, however, with a much smaller dish. Some Ku band equipment can operate with a dish as small as 3 feet in diameter, with 18-inch dishes under development.

Ku band satellite is also finding favor among users with widely scattered remote locations due to its ease of installation and low cost. These

Figure 19 Microwave transmission is also used for other applications; in this case, it is used to bring cable television to the outlying area of Ovilla, TX. (Courtesy of Premiere Network Services, Inc., Dallas, TX.)

include hotel chains, retailers, and other service bureaus utilizing sporadic data transmissions in their daily operations.

One 36-MHz satellite channel, or "transponder," is used for one full-motion color video signal. Typical network television feeds occupy a full transponder. There are 24 transponders per satellite. A transponder can also be used for transmitting digital signals. One transponder equals three DS-3 (45 Mb) bit streams, or about 2000 voice channels. Video for applications such as video conferencing need not occupy an entire transponder. A single DS-3 for example can provide near-network quality video, while a single T1 can provide quality suitable for many video teleconferencing applications.

Slow scan video is even possible at the 56 kb level. At the slower speeds, it simply takes longer to "paint" the screen each time an object moves. As can be seen by these channel capacities, a large amount of data can be carried on a single satellite transponder. Proper planning can turn a satellite link normally used for video conferencing into a "lifeline" with which to restore operations.

There are some disadvantages to satellite, the most notable of which is response time delay. Since a satellite orbits at an altitude of 25,000 miles above the equator, a signal has a roundtrip of 50,000 miles from point A to point B. This translates into a "delay" of about a third of a second from end to end. (This includes a one-way trip and also the effect of circuitry on the signal.) This delay can be a problem because not all polling protocols used for data transmission handle the delay equally well.

Some bisynchronous protocols, for example, only send a few bits to the far end before expecting an answer back. After receiving the acknowledgment, they send another few bits and wait again. This continues until a document is printed, or a CRT screen is painted, or whatever. On a normal circuit, this happens at the speed of light over a distance of a few hundred or few thousand miles; it happens so quickly that it is indiscernible to users. With satellites, however, each transmit–acknowledge cycle equates to about two-thirds of a second and it may require many cycles to complete one transaction. Thus, the system grinds virtually to a halt.

There are, however, solutions, one of which is to utilize a protocol that sends more data out before expecting an answer. This reduces the required number of cycles and speeds things up greatly. Another solution is simply to throw bandwidth at the problem. Where a 9.6 kb terrestrial circuit might normally suffice, a 56 kb circuit will pipe five times the volume of data in the same length of time, and often for close to the same cost (because satellite bandwidth is less expensive than the same speed of land line). Again, the result is the same, the polling process is faster.

A few applications still exist, however, for which a satellite is not suitable at all, such as for older equipment utilizing unforgiving protocols.

(1) What Is a Teleport?

The term "teleport" was coined by a New York–New Jersey based group that began offering satellite up-link services in the early 1980s. It caught on with the media and in investment circles, and with the help of some exposure in the *Wall Street Journal* and other publications, the name stuck.

Today there are many teleport facilities in the United States offering a number of services. In addition to satellite services, these teleports also dabble in local access, cable television, real estate, and other areas.

New York Teleport, for example, was formed by Merrill Lynch Company. It also holds a franchise granted by the New York Port Authority that has allowed it to pull fiber optic cable throughout Manhattan. The original purpose for the company, satellite transmission, is largely subcontracted. The company instead is concentrating on being a "second local access company," which has proven to be much more lucrative. New York Teleport is also constructing a second system in Boston.

Other teleports include:

1. Pacific Telecom Teleports
   - Bay Area
   - UpSouth
   - National Gateway
2. United Video, Tulsa, OK
   - Venture with Chicago Teleport. United Video is a cable television provider.
3. I.D.B., Los Angeles, CA
4. Texas Teleport of Houston
   - Is said to have a fleet of "transportables."
5. Dallas/Ft. Worth Teleport (see Fig. 20)
   - Owned by large real-estate developer, intended as an amenity to tenant base.

(2) The Dallas/Ft. Worth Teleport

Services provided by the Dallas/Ft. Worth (D/FW) Teleport are typical of those offered in the industry and include:

- C and Ku band transmitting and receiving facilities
- Transportable up-links and down-links
- Voice, data, and video services
- Microwave access links
- VSAT (shared hub) services
- Transponder sales
- International access
- Consulting and planning.

As is the case with many teleports, the D/FW Teleport has a large metropolitan area network, which serves a number of common carrier POPs and large corporate locations (see Figs. 21 and 22). In many cases facilities such as these can provide redundant access to other Bell serving offices, common carrier POPs, and a full array of satellite services, allowing for greater flexibility in a communication disaster. (Notice that connectivity exists to both AT&T and Bell serving offices.)

You will need to determine, as with common carrier POPs, that the facilities are the proper type. If they are analog, a special piece of equipment called a CODEC would be required in order to carry T1 traffic. There is also the chance that because they are designed for broadcasting, the facilities are only one-way.

The D/FW Teleport utilized microwave for its metropolitan area network due to the large physical size of the Dallas/Ft. Worth area. The New York Teleport, on the other hand, is almost exclusively fiber due to

Figure 20 The Dallas/Ft. Worth Teleport. (Courtesy of the Dallas/Ft. Worth Teleport, Irving, TX.)

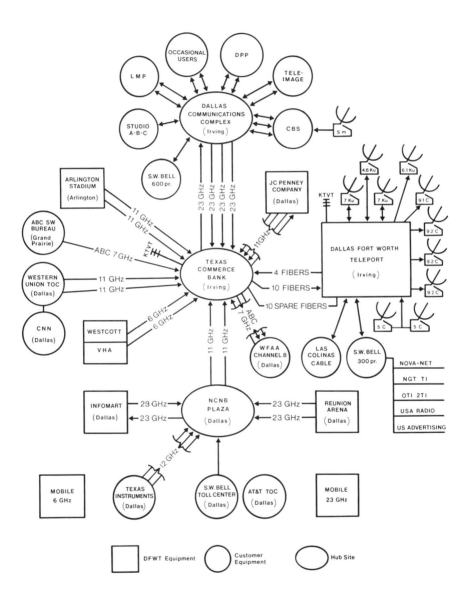

Figure 21 The Dallas/Ft. Worth Teleport operational metropolitan area network. (Courtesy of D/FW Teleport.)

DALLAS FORT WORTH TELEPORT OCCASIONAL RATES

EFFECTIVE JANUARY 1, 1990

SUBJECT TO CHANGE WITHOUT NOTICE

TYPE OF SERVICE

	30 MIN.		1ST HOUR	
Uplink & Interconnect from:	**C-Band**	**Ku-Band**	**C-Band**	**Ku-Band**
Teleport	95.00	150.00	140.00	225.00
Texas Commerce Bank	120.00	175.00	165.00	250.00
Dallas Communications Complex	125.00	180.00	195.00	280.00
INFOMART	225.00	285.00	340.00	425.00
NCNB	160.00	220.00	240.00	325.00
Reunion Arena	290.00	345.00	440.00	525.00
Arlington Stadium	315.00	365.00	475.00	560.00
SW Bell or AT&T TOC	255.00	315.00	385.00	470.00
Western Union POP at Teleport	120.00	175.00	165.00	250.00
Downlink and Interconnect to:				
Teleport	70.00	100.00	100.00	180.00
Dallas Communications Complex	100.00	135.00	155.00	235.00

ADDITIONAL SERVICES

Tape Playback and Record:	**30 MIN.**	**1ST HOUR**
Beta Playback	------	50.00 (1 Hr. Minimum)
3/4" Tape	------	50.00 (1 Hr. Minimum)
1" Tape	75.00	120.00
2" Tape Available Upon Request	------	------
Character Generator	------	25.00 (Minimum)

Customer Use of TOC Facility $25 Per hour/$125 Per day

Portable Microwave One-Hop   From $1,200 Per day single thread
From $1,500 Per day redundant microwave, includes construction
Additional day prices available

Satellite Turnarounds	$100 per 30 Min.	$180 per Hour

* Contract service rates and transponder time are available upon request.
* Bulk discounts available to End-User only.
* Audio/data transmission services available upon request.
* International transponder arrangements available upon request.
* Payment terms net 30 days with pre-approved credit.

Cancellation policy: 8 days notice, no charge; 2 - 7 days notice, 50% charge; less than 48 hours notice, 100% charge.

Figure 22 The Dallas/Ft. Worth Teleport's occasional rate schedule. (Courtesy of D/FW Teleport.)

the smaller physical area covered, and to the difficulty involved in licensing microwave frequencies in the New York metropolitan area. Transmission mediums and services offered will vary depending on which teleport is selected. If there is a teleport in your area, it would be a good idea to find out what services are available, and how they might fit into your overall recovery plan.

5.8 USE OF CELLULAR FOR RECOVERY

Another technology that holds promise in the area of network recovery is cellular technology. Until recently, there have been a number of significant drawbacks to using cellular to any large extent in a major communication disaster:

1. Cell sites (transmitters serving a given section of a metropolitan area) can easily become overwhelmed or "saturated" during a disaster. For example, one large corporate user in an affected area, activating even a moderate number of transportables, can easily saturate a cell and block other callers.
2. Most cellular systems cannot support dial-up data above 1200 b/s due to frequent switching between cells and the physical limitations of the system.
3. Cellular services are still connected to local EOs. The Hinsdale fire in Chicago was in a local EO and one cellular company was affected by it. The second cellular company was connected in a different CO, but could have experienced a similar fate.

Despite these limitations, cellular companies are viewing themselves more and more as what they actually are—a second franchised telephone company. As such, they are exploring other options beyond standard mobile telephone service. A few include:

1. *Further refinement of cellular systems* to facilitate higher speed data transmission. This not only has applications for disaster recovery, it could also be quite marketable. A route salesman, for example, could use a pocket terminal and mobile phone service to enter orders while at a customer's store or other location. (*See* Calhoun, G., *Digital Cellular Radio,* Artech House, 1988.)
2. *Development of cellular modems.* These are already available if you are willing look for them.
3. *Cellular "vans"* are available in many areas for response to local disasters.
4. *T1 and other enhanced services.* This development is very exciting. In December 1988, through *Auxiliary Services General Docket 87-*

390, the Federal Communication Commission (FCC) authorized mobile telephone companies to provide T1 service in the cellular frequency band.

Potential uses for these T1 services might include:

- Alternative T1 local loops (for local access diversity)
- "On demand" T1 local loops
- Disaster recovery links for the cellular companies themselves, such as for drawing dial tones from other COs in a central office disaster.

Cellular companies may even begin to sell "T1 options" to large corporate users. In the event of a CO or local facility disaster, the cellular company would divert bandwidth from the nearest cell site to activate one or more emergency T1s for a large subscribing user. At the same time, they would divert additional bandwidth from adjoining cell sites to take up the slack for the first cell site. This would allow the response time in a disaster to be as fast as the time it takes to run a predetermined computer program at the main cellular serving office. For this guarantee, the corporate user could pay a monthly retainer fee, as with a "hot site," creating an additional revenue stream for the mobile phone company.

Chapter 6
Assessing Vulnerability in the Local Serving Office

6.1 STARTING THE ASSESSMENT PROCESS

For most companies, another "choke point" for the network is the local telephone serving office for their area. In most cases, all data and voice traffic must pass through this location on its first leg to the remote customer. The physical capabilities and configurations of these local offices vary greatly. The size and density of the serving area for the office also varies substantially from CO to CO.

One of the easiest ways to become familiar with the service area of a particular local CO is to pick up a local telephone directory and look at the first few pages. There is usually a diagram that illustrates the local calling area and exchanges served in the immediate area (see Fig. 23; the scale may not be exact, but it gives a good indication). It does provide, however, information on the *relative* size of the service area for each CO and usually will list the telephone prefixes (NXX codes) for the area. It also has the advantage of being easily understandable for the beginner. (As stated earlier, a solution need not be beautiful to be functional!)

For example, in looking at Fig. 23, notice that a company with a 231 telephone prefix is served out of the Richardson CO. It also shows at a glance which telephone company serves which area. By comparing this map to a regular city map, it is possible to get an idea of how many other companies are served out of your area's local telephone office. This could have a bearing on recovery time in the event of a severe CO outage.

There are a few problems, however, with depending solely on a diagram like this one. For one thing, a few of the areas defined have more

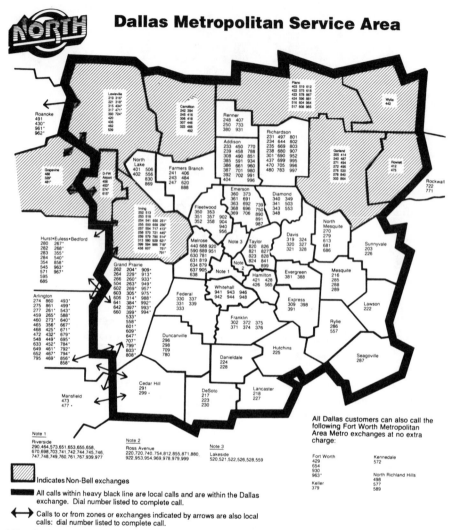

Figure 23 Dallas metropolitan service area. (Courtesy of Southwestern Bell Telephone Company.)

than one CO. Farmers Branch, for example, has two, but there is no way to determine this from Fig. 23. While this diagram is a good starting point and serves as a general overview, it is sketchy and does not have nearly enough detail to make a worthwhile analysis.

There are other sources that provide more detailed, complete information that is suitable to network analysis. One such source in the United States is the Public Service Commission (PSC) for each state. The PSC is the repository of a wealth of information on this subject for those willing to do some digging.

6.2 UTILIZING STATE PUBLIC SERVICE COMMISSION RECORDS

Local exchange companies are required to keep detailed maps, diagrams, and other information regarding their franchise areas on file with the individual states' PSCs. There are obvious reasons for this, such as formally defining service areas, as well as other reasons. For instance, local calling areas must be defined meticulously because they can vary from city to city, exchange to exchange, and even CO to CO. Figures 24 and 25 illustrate some of the types of information available from the PSC.

Useful data on file can include the following.

1. Definition of the serving area for every central office in the state, down to the particular street, and in many cases down to the foot is provided. From this information, you can tell immediately which municipalities are served by which office. (In many cases different sides of a street may be served by different COs.) In Fig. 25, for example, you can see that the De Soto CO serves not only the City of De Soto, but Glenn Heights and portions of Ovilla as well.

   The area served by this CO extends between two counties, Dallas and Ellis counties. Major thoroughfares (Houston School Road, Pleasant Run Road, and Duncanville Road) have been used as physical boundaries on the northeast, east, and west sides of the De Soto zone, while other boundaries are imaginary lines. This could all be valuable information if a disaster were to affect this particular CO. Among other things, you could tell how far an employee would have to drive to find a working phone in the event of a failure in the CO.

2. Definition of exchange boundaries and local calling scopes is also provided in commission records. While this may not be of direct consequence to disaster recovery, it definitely has a bearing on business planning. One large company located itself just outside the Houston metropolitan calling area. As a result, it now incurs many thousands of dollars in additional toll charges that are not applicable to even its close neighbors. Consequently, the company had to fight a long battle in the Texas Public Utility Commission for extended area service (EAS) to the Houston metropolitan area—a long and arduous process.

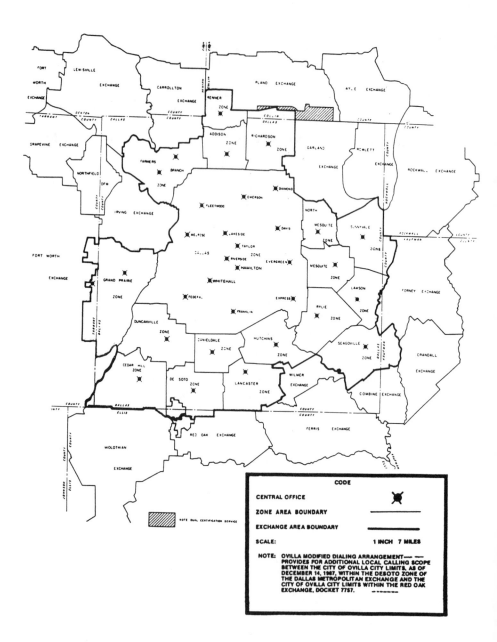

Figure 24 Dallas metropolitan exchange area map.

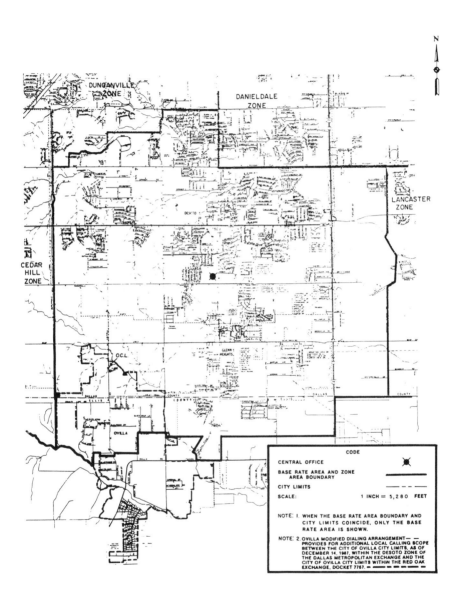

Figure 25 De Soto zone area and base rate area map.

While telephone service is not the only factor to consider in locating a business, it certainly can be significant and should be evaluated.

3. Information on proposed new serving offices in a given area is also on file at the PSC. While these proposals are usually announced well in advance by the telephone companies, they require much preplanning within a large corporation. For example, looking back on Fig. 24, the Renner zone (on the north side) is a relatively new serving office. This change meant that, for customers in this area, telephone numbers recently changed and circuit loop costs on private line circuits were rerated, based on the new distance to the downtown toll center.

While these are usually relatively minor inconveniences, they do require planning. Users may want to keep their old telephone numbers, for example. Also, the newly assigned telephone prefix may not be updated in a timely fashion in PBX equipment at other locations, which results in some users not being able to call the new numbers.

The information available from the commission aids the planning effort and makes changes of this sort less disruptive by providing advance notice. PSC information can also be a useful barometer of when Non-Conforming End Offices (NCEOs) will be upgraded, allowing your company access to other carriers and modern CO features.

4. Distances to other serving offices can often be approximated through the use of available documents, which could be important for companies considering diversity through "special construction" of facilities at another serving office. Quite naturally, the cost of such a project will vary with the distance and availability of existing cable or fiber.

Distance, however, is not the only consideration. The closest CO, for instance, may not contain the technology needed by the customer. (For instance, some may not be able to provide digital services.) It may even be operated by a different local operating company—a difficult prospect in both the construction phase and in future circuit coordination. In any case, the information on file with the PSC can aid in decisions of this type also.

5. Finally, these records typically contain information on how close to capacity a given CO is. While rare, COs do occasionally reach capacity in the number of dial telephone circuits they can provide, which may necessitate service delays. Likely candidates for a shortage are often NCEOs scheduled for switch replacement in the near

future. The telephone company is naturally reluctant to invest more than is required in the outmoded switch, so they often ride the edge and have less surplus capacity than is typical in other offices. Information on pending switch replacements may also be available from the PSC.

In summary, when beginning a study of the company's local serving office, start simple.

1. Get an overview from your phone book, telephone company representative, or other readily available and easily understandable source.
2. Utilize resources available at the PSC such as maps, charts, capacity projections, and other suggested items.
3. Establish a rapport with commission staff members. Relationships with these individuals can be rewarding for both parties. Much information is available in the public domain that is valuable to the network contingency planner. Having an experienced "guide" to help you through the maze of bureaucracy will help greatly.

Likewise, commission staff members, as government employees, can often be isolated from what is happening in their areas of jurisdiction. "Outsiders" bring new technologies and ideas with them that help keep the staff abreast of technological changes. This helps them do their jobs as regulators better. Liaisons of this type can be quite fruitful.

6.3 ASSESSING CENTRAL OFFICE PHYSICAL SECURITY

Physically, most local serving offices are sound structures constructed of reinforced concrete. Because designs vary, you should definitely drive by the serving office. Look for the obvious. Does the structure have a large portion of the surface area covered by windows? Does it appear to be in an area that could be prone to periodic flooding? Is there major construction activity planned or occurring in the immediate area around the CO? (See Figs. 26 and 27.)

Ask some questions of your telephone company's account representative. Is the CO manned 24 hours a day? What type of fire prevention systems does it employ? How old is the structure? One item most operating companies are quite willing to provide is a CO tour. In addition to being able to survey your network's repository first-hand, there are other benefits.

One benefit is the ability to meet the people who will install or work on your circuits face to face. Many communication managers will tell you

Figure 26 Beware! Construction activity this close to a critical EO should be grounds for concern. (Courtesy of Premiere Network Services, Inc., Dallas, TX.)

Figure 27 In this particular case, the main telephone plant was exposed to construction, but it was being conducted by Southwestern Bell itself, so there was reason to breathe easier. Even so, telephone company contractors often cut cables in the course of construction. (Courtesy of Premiere Network Services, Inc., Dallas, TX.)

how much easier it is to resolve further service problems when they can speak with "Bob," the telecommunication guy they had lunch with from the CO. "Bob," of course, also gets a good sense of the urgency involved in your company's service. After all, to Bob it may be "just another 56 kb circuit." To your company, it may be Eastern Division Headquarters.

When you consider the fact that Bob works on perhaps three dozen problem cases per day, all of them critical, faces and names count.

After your tour through the CO, discuss security plans for the CO with your telecommunication representative. Although it will probably take some probing, try to get answers to questions like:

1. Is the CO a tandem or end office? What plans exist for restoration in the event of fire and flood? What services would be affected?

2. How difficult or expensive would it be for facilities to be brought in from another CO? Occasionally bringing in alternative facilities is reasonably straightforward, but often it is prohibitively expensive, if not impossible.

   One alternative can be Foreign Central Office (FCO) or Foreign Exchange (FX) service. This type of switched service does not pass through the local switch itself, since the dial tone is provided from a remote CO. The circuit will, however, pass through the physical structure of the CO. A switch failure in the local CO will not cripple FX or FCO service. A total loss of a CO (for example, to a flood or tornado), however, is another story (see Fig. 28). In Chicago's Hinsdale disaster, for example, many users lost dial service entirely, but some FX lines kept functioning since they were not served out of the damaged switch.

3. Try to get an idea of the topology of the entire city's telephone network. Is it a hubbing or nonhubbing configuration? (See Fig. 29.) While hubbing is more economical for the telephone company because facilities are better utilized, it does not provide the protection that interoffice tandem trunks provide in nonhubbing configurations.

   Again, using the Hinsdale disaster as a gauge, only about a quarter of the traffic destined for the devastated CO could be diverted via tandem trunks. In a disaster, the more of these that exist to absorb the increased traffic load from a crippled CO the better.

4. Ask about the regional serving offices and access tandems. Is all toll traffic concentrated through the regional access tandem office (common in smaller, outlying areas) or split among a number of EOs?

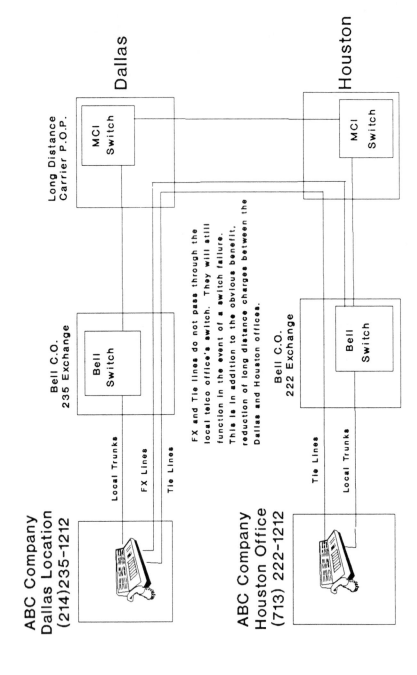

Figure 28 Use of FX and tie lines for switch diversity.

Non-Hubbing

Major Advantage:

Better Fault Tolerance

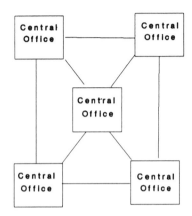

Hubbing

Major Advantage:

Lower Cost and Better Utilization of Facilities

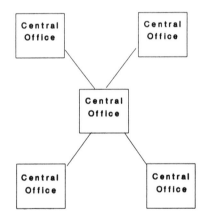

Figure 29 CO hubbing configurations. How well a CO survives a major facility disaster depends largely on how it is engineered into the overall network.

Chapter 7
Contingency Planning Within the Bell Operating Companies

7.1 "POST-HINSDALE" RECOMMENDATIONS

Chicago's Hinsdale CO disaster underscored the fallibility of telephone switching centers. In the aftermath of the disaster, most of the Bell operating companies (BOCs) and many of the independents launched their own investigations to ensure that their respective houses were in order.

One such study, commissioned by Southwestern Bell Telephone Company, examined CO vulnerability issues. A report issued after the study made specific recommendations for avoiding a similar disaster. These included, among other recommendations:

1. Sprinklers in cable areas
2. Separation of power and telephone cables
3. Improved surge protection equipment
4. dc power disconnect equipment
5. Management of combustibles in the CO
6. Smoke removal capabilities in larger COs
7. Special walls around certain equipment areas that are designed to keep a fire from spreading
8. Training and retraining of fire prevention personnel
9. Procedures for calling the fire department upon dispatch of a local operating company to investigate a fire, not after.
10. Tours for fire fighters
11. More 24-hour personnel coverage.

Surprisingly, the use of Halon fire protection systems in COs was often not recommended, primarily due to cost and environmental concerns. The study also made note of that fact that there has not been a significant fire in Southwestern Bell territory in more than 25 years.

Southwestern Bell has proposed implementing these and other steps in some 20 major network hubs during 1990. (In Southwestern Bell's five-state area, some 1300 COs are currently under its control.) By the end of 1991, Southwestern Bell expects to extend these recommendations to another 70 COs. Similar measures have been taken in other BOCs.

In any event, interest in the area of contingency planning has risen markedly in all seven Bell companies since the Hinsdale incident. Overall, the attitude of these companies toward protection of both their assets and the services of their customers has been remarkably good. The question is whether the level of protection offered by BOCs and the level to which most corporations are accustomed within their own businesses is the same.

A financial services firm, for example, may spend millions of dollars on elaborate Halon fire suppression and security systems to ensure the continuity of operations only to be crippled by an incident beyond its control such as a CO fire. Thus far, the Bell companies have adopted the attitude that they will do whatever is required by the end-user and that the expense is secondary. The question, of course, is from where will the money come? The argument can be made that what a large corporation considers as a normal and reasonable level of protection might be considered extravagant by the typical telephone user.

Should Halon suppression systems be installed in COs? Should additional facilities be built to allow diversion of switched traffic from one CO to another in a disaster? Should the cost of these improvements be added to the rate base, forcing large users, small users, and residential users to share the cost? Who ultimately should pay?

For the time being, until these issues are better defined, the answer is that the *affected user* pays, individually.

If your corporation considers a major telephone outage an inconvenience rather than a disaster, contingency planning for your network is probably not a major issue. If your company, however, is totally reliant on the phone—as many are—your responsibility is to eliminate any vulnerability. This is accomplished by alerting the local operating company to your firm's special needs, and by working with them on a solution such as special construction to an alternative serving office. It might also involve securing alternative facilities on your own. The important thing to remember is that the well-being of the company is at stake. Blaming the phone company is no longer an excuse in today's telecommunication-dependent corporations.

7.2 REDUNDANCY IN HIGH VOLUME CORPORATE NETWORKS

Some of the most difficult network disaster recoveries involve communication carriers. Consider cellular service providers. Many of these companies have the worst of both worlds when it comes to backup in the event of a disaster; namely, extremely long intervals for switching equipment replacement and a customer base that can defect easily to the "other" cellular provider in the event its provider fails.

In the example above, the risk of disaster to a cellular company is significant, even though there are only two franchised providers in a metropolitan area. What about other areas of telecommunication where the market is many times more competitive? Long-distance companies that experience major failures can be bypassed easily by users dialing 10XXX codes for other carriers. If the failure persists for days or weeks, most of these customers will probably sign on with another carrier, possibly never to return. The revenue implications here are obvious.

Communication carriers stand to lose a lot in a disaster because of the complexity of network recovery and the highly competitive nature of their industry. Because commercial backup facilities for carriers are nonexistent, only a few other options remain:

1. Signing mutual aid agreements with other carriers.
2. Maintaining a high level of redundancy and protection in the network.

The first option is difficult to apply, both from a technical and a competitive standpoint. Discussions are being held between some carriers in this area, and for the first time the discussions include AT&T. Competition in the industry, however, will make it difficult to work out any meaningful backup plans between carriers. "Gentlemen's agreements" between carriers are probably the best we can hope for in this area for the foreseeable future.

This leaves the second option, maintaining a high degree of protection in the network. This can be accomplished cost effectively through thoughtful engineering of the network. The following is a good example.

Next to AT&T, International Telecharge Inc. (ITI) is the second largest provider of long-distance operator services in the United States. Its major clients include hospitals, hotels, and other large users in the hospitality industry. Like most other long-distance companies, ITI operates in a fiercely competitive climate that necessitates a high degree of network availability and service quality. This environment has not only mandated that adequate network safeguards be in place, it has required that these safeguards be applied to the huge volumes of traffic typical of a major long-distance provider.

Figure 30 illustrates the local access network of ITI in Dallas. The main purpose for its inclusion here is to demonstrate that even the highest volume telecommunication users can design adequate and cost-effective network safeguards through thoughtful engineering. The most notable items in the figure include:

1. ITI utilizes two common carrier (MCI) POPs. This provides backup in the event of a major failure by allowing for the splitting of traffic between POPs.

2. Redundant access links serve each of the above POPs. Because these are provided by private access companies, there are no common CO facilities involved.

3. Redundant access links (fiber and microwave) are installed between ITI's downtown switch and its outlying Operator Service Center, approximately 11 miles away. (This center supports in excess of 1400 operators.)

4. Southwestern Bell, Metrolink Fiber, and Metropolitan Fiber Systems are part of this network, for a total of three local access vendors, negating the possibility that failure of a single vendor would cause a catastrophic outage.

5. Access to three EAEOs is possible from various points in the network. These are indicated in Fig. 30 by the small boxes labeled "SWB FL" (Fleetwood), "SWB RI" (Riverside), and "SWB RO" (Ross). All three of these facilities are major downtown serving offices. Direct Bell-owned tandem trunking probably exists between the three, which could be used to access MCI should a disaster strike in any one of the three. In fact, even if the Access Tandem itself were incapacitated, some service could be restored in this fashion via one of the EOs shown. Line-of-sight transmission for emergency microwave from several points in town is also possible. The ITI technical staff is familiar with use of this technology by virtue of the Operator Center's microwave link. Through these methods, ITI should always be able to reach an MCI POP, even if capacity were to be reduced.

6. Finally, it is virtually impossible for a single facility failure to isolate the Operator Center or ITI switch from the MCI network. Figure 31 illustrates that although up to 60% of the network could be affected by a single facility failure, critical functions of the business could continue.

In ITI's case, there were no simple solutions. The access arrangement shown was designed as a "custom" network in the truest sense of the word. Even the T-3 access links provided by the Bell company were secured on a special construction basis. This required a high level of support and

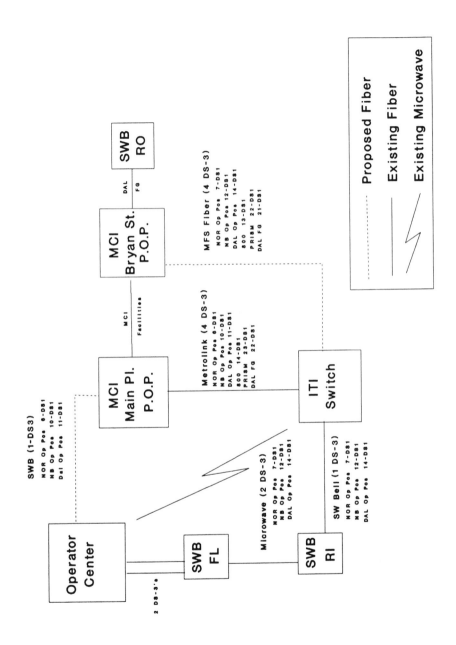

Figure 30 ITI's Dallas area T-3 network.

Routing Splits

Operator Position Trunks (Op Pos)		MCI Access	
Microwave Link	40%	Metrolink Fiber	50%
Fiber	60%	Metropolitan Fiber Systems (MFS)	50%
ITI Switch to Operator Center	30%		
MCI Main PL to Operator Center	30%		

The ITI DS-3 network has been designed to eliminate common failure points in order to maintain network integrity. The enormous volume of circuit traffic posed a significant, but not insurmountable engineering task for the ITI staff.

Figure 31 ITI route splits. (Courtesy of ITI, Dallas, TX.)

involvement on the part of the telecommunications staff. The benefits, however, have been great. ITI enjoys a fault-tolerant, high quality, low cost, access system that provides both quality service to ITI users and peace of mind to the company.

Chapter 8
Common Communication Disasters

8.1 CABLE CUTS—HOW TO PROTECT AGAINST "BACKHOE FADE"

Without a doubt, the most prevalent form of communication "disaster" is the accidental disruption of buried telecommunication cables. While the reliability of buried transmission media far surpasses that of its aerial counterpart, it is vulnerable by nature, as Fig. 32 illustrates.

8.2 ASSESSING COMMUNICATION RIGHTS-OF-WAY

Telephone, electric, fiber optic, gas, water, television cables, and other utilities are most often installed in the same public rights-of-way, mainly along streets and thoroughfares. In many U.S. cities, particularly older ones like New York, Boston, and Philadelphia, these rights-of-way date back quite a number of years. As a result, when a contractor digs to repair or install facilities, he is often never quite sure what he will find on the way down.

While being underground makes a telephone cable facility more secure in one way, in another way, ironically, it becomes more vulnerable. Accurate record keeping is usually a problem when rights-of-way have been in continuous use for decades or more. Being off even a few inches with a backhoe can have devastating consequences to buried utilities of all types. During the mid-1980s heyday of fiber construction by AT&T, Sprint, and other companies, the frequency with which these companies' contractors cut each other's (or their own) cables was almost comical. Again, it is all part of the risk of using public rights-of-way.

During recent years, some companies have utilized some very innovative schemes for installing communication facilities. Fiber has been laid in abandoned steam tunnels, subway tunnels, and other public rights-of-way. While this eliminates one problem by making the facility more accessible, it could be creating another by making the facility visible and susceptible to other disruptions, including tampering by unauthorized personnel or vandalism.

Other companies have used railroad rights-of-way. This has been particularly true for long-haul fiber routes. This scheme has worked well for the most part, although there have been incidents of train derailments causing cable cuts. Also, a disaster such as a toxic chemical spill resulting from a train derailment could mean an outage of significant duration.

Another innovative solution involves a common carrier who wanted to build fiber through a state park. The state agreed, on the condition that the carrier build a bicycle path over the cable route for use by residents. The carrier proceeded with the plan, and to our knowledge that was the extent of the "royalty" paid to the state. Another company had plans to lay fiber aboveground in abandoned gas pipeline and one New England based fiber carrier actually strung aerial fiber (presumably this would be risky during ice storms, but makes the fiber more accessible in winter months).

Of course, everyone has a favorite cable-cut story. Mine was probably the one where a farmer cut through a major AT&T cable route with a backhoe and then, as if to add insult to injury, mistakenly drained his stock pond into the hole. Cable cuts are no laughing matter, however, if it is your business that has to suffer through it. Losses from these incidents

Figure 32 Common communication disasters.

can range from the thousands to tens of millions of dollars per hour depending on location, severity, and type of business affected.

In assessing your company's exposure to these types of disruptions, try to get answers to the following questions from your long-haul carrier company.

1. What is the predominant transmission medium?

If it is fiber, coaxial, or other type of buried telephone plant, ask what type of rights-of-way are used for facilities serving the cities of interest to your company.

2. Do "loops" exist in the network for diversity?

Many times a carrier will route a "protection" or backup channel via a third city to provide automatic switching of facilities in the event a facility is disrupted. If such an arrangement exists, ask if it utilizes an automatic "hitless switching" arrangement or if a network center must manually activate the backup route after trouble is reported. In either case, ask how often the backup facility has been used since its inception, what the duration of outage was during the disruption, and if the reroute plan is ever tested between outages.

3. Does the long-haul carrier serve its own POPs in the city where you will be using them, or does it use Bell facilities on the last leg of the long-haul cable into the city?

One perfectly acceptable practice is for a carrier to lease Bell DS-3 capacity from its long-haul route to a metropolitan POP to avoid paying expensive rights-of-way and construction charges. Although this arrangement can make the long-haul carrier susceptible to disruptions in or between the metropolitan Bell COs through which the DS-3 facility passes, it would not be a serious disruption, but it does need to be factored into your company's recovery plans. After all, most cable cuts take place in busy urban areas where a lot of construction takes place.

4. Does the carrier have a good performance record?

Some carriers may just have had bad luck, but one with frequent service disruptions may have made a bad right-of-way choice for its fiber.

5. Does the carrier have interconnection arrangements with other carriers in the event of major failures?

Exclusive of AT&T, there have been repeated instances over the years of competing carriers coming to each other's aid during major facility disruptions. Since competing carriers often collocate within the same buildings in many cities, they are often inclined to "grab" ten T1s or a DS-3 from a competitor until their network is repaired. Moves are afoot, however, to formalize such mutual aid agreements, and for the first time AT&T is involved in the dialogue.

8.3 OTHER POINTS OF NETWORK VULNERABILITY

Analysis of vulnerability in communication sometimes fails to consider even the most obvious. Would a medium-sized suburban company be prepared to deal with a day-long communication outage because a driver took down a pole or ran over a critical telephone pedestal? These events do not make headlines, but they happen thousands of times yearly and end up costing companies plenty.

Central offices and cables are not the only items to consider when assessing vulnerability in outside plant. The equipment in Fig. 33(a) is an SLC-96 Pair Gain unit. ("SLC" stands for subscriber loop carrier.) As the name implies, it is used for "pair gain." In areas where cable facilities are in short supply and distances are long (hence, construction expensive), these units are used to carry 544 simultaneous circuits on 16 pairs of copper cables. There is also a fiber version. They work exceptionally well and have been broadly accepted by the local operating companies. In fact, according to Southwestern Bell, there were 2,764,813 miles of feeder facilities served by pair gain T-carriers in Texas as of December 1988.

If a company is in an area served by one of these units, usually an outlying suburban area, it must remember that it too is uniquely vulnerable. If a driver loses control and runs a car into a CO, for example, there would probably not be much of a physical consequence other than a totaled car and some structural damage. As one can see from the photographs of Fig. 33, however, a collision with a pair gain unit would destroy the equipment and isolate users. This is the same consequence experienced during a total CO disaster, although the outage would probably be of a shorter duration because replacement times for this type of equipment are shorter.

Figure 33(a) shows significant protection for the pair gain unit in the form of a fence and pylons that are designed to absorb the impact. The second unit, Fig. 33(b), is set back from the road a safe distance. The

Figure 33 Pair gain systems and other outside plant.

third unit pictured in Fig. 33(c), however, is exposed to the traffic on a busy secondary highway. This particular unit is an SLC-40, an older vintage pair gain unit that was probably installed some years back. It is no longer manufactured and could possibly pose a problem for replacement if destroyed.

Of course, the potential exists for someone to shoot out the electric meter or for other vandalism to any of these units. The point is that you need to determine what kind of equipment is serving the area your company is in and make arrangements to eliminate exposure if possible.

In the case of the units shown in Fig. 33, they served an area where we keep an outlying office. Each of the units were within one-half mile of the other (due to growth in the community) and also sat on the same cable route. Therefore, the phone company was able to "mix" circuits easily from each unit to our remote office. Some circuits were even routed to bypass the pair gain unit entirely, even though the distance to the CO was great (more than 30,000 feet), by means of adding gain devices in the CO. The net cost of these improvements was less than $200 in installation and engineering charges.

Pair gain equipment might also find possible applications within metropolitan areas for bringing in foreign dial tone and other services from redundant COs. It eliminates many of the distance and cable facility problems associated with bringing in large numbers of circuits from COs outside a customer's central serving office. Used in this manner, pair gain units could eliminate much of the dependence on a single CO. Their use in this way, however, would require a unique set of circumstances to exist, including availability of cable pair or conduit between the serving areas of the two COs, the suitability of the cable for carrying T1, and—most important—the interest level of the telephone company. Still, local telephone companies today are taking a fresh new look at special construction arrangements and may be inclined to give such an assembly a second look. You can always ask!

Chapter 9

Engineering Techniques for the Bell Operating Companies

This chapter is based on an article by Gerd W. Printz and Kathleen C. Szelag. The authors detail a few examples of technologies available to the BOCs for maintaining a robust local exchange network. Our thanks to AT&T Bell Laboratories for making this text available.

9.1 SAFETYNET SERVICE ASSURANCE CONQUERS DISASTER*

Technological advancements have brought many efficiencies to the public network, including high capacity switching and transmission systems. The resulting high concentration of traffic in fewer network elements, however, requires new design approaches if we are to minimize the network's vulnerability to disasters. Businesses that rely increasingly on the network for new revenue and for their internal operations have rising expectations about the reliability of network service.

AT&T's SafetyNet Service Assurance offering includes integrated packages of products and services for operating companies that enables them to upgrade their networks' ability to provide uninterrupted service to customers when disaster strikes. SafetyNet packages utilize ring architectures, increased connectivity between network elements, route diversity, automatic protection switching, and rapid restoration of network elements.

---

*From Printz, G. W., and K. C. Szelag, "SafetyNet Service Assurance Conquers Disaster," *AT&T Technical Journal,* January 1990. Reprinted with permission, ©1990 AT&T Bell Laboratories.

On an average day, you may make several phone calls, and rarely do you run into any network-caused problems. If a call cannot be completed, it is usually because the called party was busy or did not answer or because you dialed incorrectly. Occasionally, on high traffic days (Mother's Day, Christmas, *et cetera*), you may get an "all circuits busy" announcement or tone. The reason for an incomplete call is very seldom the result of a major network disaster.

Disasters do happen, though. When a flood, earthquake, or fire damages or destroys a switching or transmission office, all subscribers served by that office generally cannot make or receive calls until repairs are completed. As discussed in Chapter 8, a backhoe or drill may destroy a buried cable linking two offices.

For every hour an average business's communication facilities are down, losses can amount to tens of thousands of dollars. Firms that rely heavily on data transmission may lose even more. An insurance company, for example, might lose $20,000 an hour, or an airline more than two million dollars. Investment banking houses without phone service could go out of business in a day.

Knowing that such disasters occur, many businesses are taking steps to protect themselves. They are asking for increasingly reliable service from their local and toll carriers, or are acquiring and managing their own networks for primary or backup service.

The networks being established are designed for their robustness and superior reliability. They are unlikely to fail, can automatically act to prevent certain types of failures, and can be restored to full service rapidly if a non-preventable failure occurs. Robust networks are the focus of AT&T's new SafetyNet Service Assurance offering. This set of products and services will enable regional holding companies and independent phone companies to give their customers increasingly reliable telecommunication services.

(1) Robust Interoffice Transport

A telecommunication carrier can begin to make its network more robust by upgrading interoffice facilities with high capacity lightwave systems. While each fiber optic cable typically carries from several hundred megabits per second of traffic (about 6000 voice-grade circuits) to a few gigabits per second of traffic (some 50,000 voice-grade circuits), these routes pose a new problem. Because the cable frequently is buried, it is susceptible to breakage from backhoes, drills, train derailments, and the like. Most of today's lightwave systems are engineered with a protection fiber to back up one or more service fibers. If a service fiber is cut, the system automatically and immediately switches to the protection fiber.

Unfortunately, many carriers bury both fibers together to save the expense of an alternative route. This policy would not protect against cable cuts because both fibers would probably be severed. In addition, lightwave networks today typically have little or no planned alternative routing, are often engineered on a point-to-point (as opposed to network) basis, and generally are maintained and administered manually. All these deficiencies decrease network reliability.

Instead, to increase network reliability, carriers must provide alternative routing via ring architectures, design engineering on a network basis, and increase the level of automation within the network. The SafetyNet Service Assurance offering helps carriers do these things with route diversity rings, dual-fed rings, and reconfigurable rings.

(2) Route Diversity Ring

A route diversity ring is the simplest and most direct way to protect a fiber route (see Fig. 34). With this ring, the lightwave system service channel (or channels) follows one physical path and the protection channel follows another. The two routes do not share repeater huts or manholes. A 1×1 ring often is deployed with one protection channel backing up each service channel. If a cable is cut, 100% of the traffic is restorable within the operating time (less than 50 milliseconds) of the automatic-protection

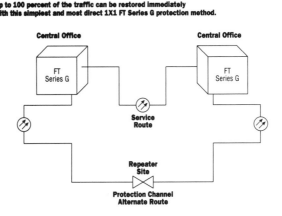

Figure 34 Route diversity ring.

switch. Also, one protection channel may back up several service channels. With a 1×4 ring, 25% of the traffic can be restored immediately.

Route diversity rings are used when the carrier wishes to protect the entire lightwave route and has available an alternative path between the originating and terminating offices. Restoration is fast and automatic. Because route diversity rings are dedicated to one lightwave system, it is difficult for the carrier to use the spare protection channel for any other purpose than backup of the original service line.

Such rings may be expensive because their protection channel not only duplicates the electronics of the service channel, but also requires its own fiber transport and repeaters. The alternative route often is more than twice the length of the service line, doubling the fiber cost. The increased route length may also cause a technical problem in the lightwave telemetry systems. Most lightwave systems are designed with the service and protection routes having the same number of repeaters. That is not the case if the two routes are different lengths—a design that will cause phase shift between signals.

The solution is a lightwave system such as AT&T's FT Series G. This system can be operated in an unbalanced mode; that is, with a different number of repeaters in the service and protection routes. Carriers sometimes want the full and fast restoration of a route diversity ring but either cannot economically justify protecting the entire lightwave system, or they have one or two key customers requiring reliable transport. The answer may be a dual-fed ring (see Fig. 35).

(3) Dual-Fed Ring

An FT Series G lightwave system with a ring diversity switch (RDS) produces a dual-fed ring. This new option for the lightwave system duplicates a 45 Mb/s signal coming into it and sends both signals over two different routes. At the receiving end, another ring diversity switch selects the better of the two signals for transmission to the customer. If the fiber in the main route is cut, the duplicate signal on the other route is available immediately. Or, if the quality of the signal on one route is degraded, the RDS automatically switches to the better signal.

A dual-fed ring can also connect several offices. Assume that with a three-office network the traffic levels between any two offices are as shown in Fig. 35. The capacity of the dual-fed ring is then the sum of all these point-to-point loads, with all traffic routed completely around the ring. Both the route diversity ring and the dual-fed ring are fully automatic. Craft or operations system intervention is not required to activate the protection switch.

A few facility nodes with small point-to-point demand can be more economically linked for full automatic protection in a ring using FT Series G ring diversity switches.

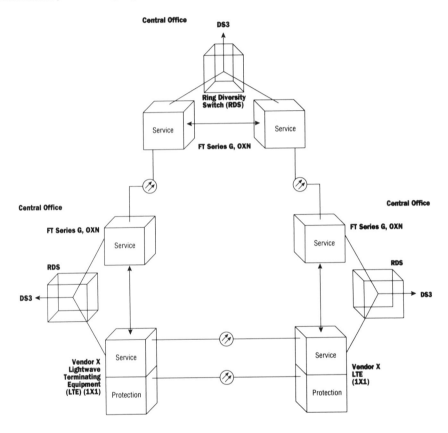

Figure 35 Dual-fed ring.

(4) The Reconfigurable Ring

A carrier may choose to install and operate a reconfigurable ring (see Fig. 36). While both the route diversity ring and the dual-fed ring have the advantages of operating simplicity and operation in milliseconds, they also have limitations in certain types of networks. They may be expensive,

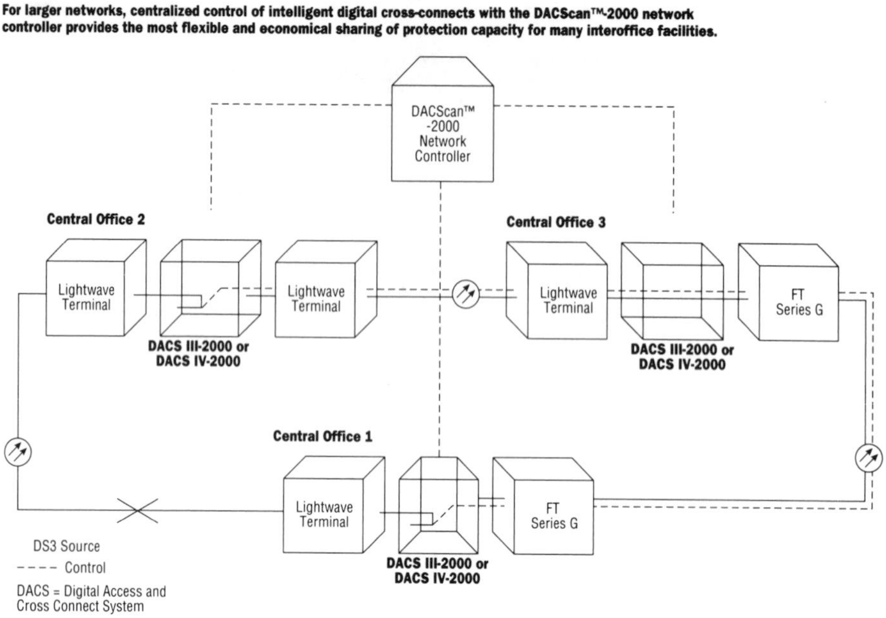

For larger networks, centralized control of intelligent digital cross-connects with the DACScan™-2000 network controller provides the most flexible and economical sharing of protection capacity for many interoffice facilities.

Figure 36 Reconfigurable ring.

particularly in large networks, and the spare capacity added to protect each route is dedicated to that route.

A reconfigurable ring, in contrast, allows the carrier to add some spare capacity in the network for restoration. The ring, however, also gives the network flexibility to reuse this restoration capacity to protect several spans. Reconfigurable rings typically are based on high speed electronic cross-connect systems such as AT&T's DACS III-2000 and DACS IV-2000.

Assume, for example, that a network of three transmission facility hubs is built with a DACS III-2000 in each hub. DACS III-2000 has access to each 45 Mb/s signal in lightwave systems within the office. Suppose that the fiber between offices 1 and 2 is cut. The intelligent cross-connects in offices 1 and 2 can be preprogrammed to connect in the 2–3–1 route until the 1–2 route is repaired. When route 1–2 is repaired, the same cross-connects return route 2–3–1 in its backup status.

Another advantage of reconfigurable rings is that they lend themselves well to central control. One such controller is the DACScan 2000 Network Controller, currently under development. When put into service, the DACScan controller will be able to issue commands to and read messages from AT&T's cross-connect systems and those of other vendors. Using a controller, the network provider will be able to provision 1.5 Mb/s and 45 Mb/s circuits more quickly to speed up circuit restoration.

(5) Robust Interexchange Access

A special concern to customers and carriers is making sure the customer can make inter-LATA calls. Since divestiture, interexchange carriers have obtained switched-access trunks from the local exchange provider. If traffic on these trunks is disrupted, the end customer will not be able to make long-distance calls, the local exchange provider will be deprived of revenue from the interexchange carrier, and the interexchange carrier will be deprived of the customers' long-distance revenue. The total revenue loss can be huge. Local exchange revenue from interexchange carrier access amounted to more that $26 billion in 1987.

As explained earlier, the local exchange carrier and interexchange carrier currently connect at meeting points called POPs. Both carriers are now exploring new tariff and network configurations to determine which will make their "trunk meet" more reliable. The simplest approach to improving reliability is alternative routing, which may be done in two ways. One is local exchange carrier diverse routing to a single POP. The other is dual-homing (Fig. 37) of one local exchange carrier office to two interexchange carrier POPs.

Special arrangements are also being considered, such as transfer arrangements and automatic loop transfer. In a transfer service (either key or dial-up), service is transferred to a second channel if the primary carrier local exchange carrier–interexchange carrier channel is disrupted.

(6) Robust Access for the End-Customer

Since the dawn of the telecommunication industry, the star architecture has been used in the public network between the customer premises and the local serving wire center. Called the "loop plant," this part of the network has consisted of dedicated copper wire pairs between the wire center and each telephone.

Because telecommunication is becoming so critical to so many businesses, the star architecture is no longer considered sufficiently reliable. For these businesses, a fundamental change to dual-homing is needed in the loop plant architecture. With dual-homing, there are two diverse transmission routes from each critical customer location to two separate wire centers served by two separate switching EOs. The extra costs associated

All single network points of failure can be eliminated using
the 5ESS® switch's distributed architecture and diverse loop access.

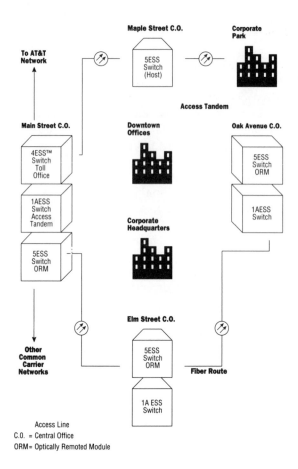

Figure 37 Dual-homing for switched services.

with dual-homing may be borne initially by the individual customers. Later, the loop portion of the network will use the same design as the interoffice portion, and costs can be shared among customers.

To satisfy the need for dependable public switched services, phone companies can install the remote switching modules of the 5ESS switch on the customer's premises. Or the modules can be installed in neighboring COs so that service is provided by one logically connected 5ESS switch.

These modules have substantial stand-alone capability, which preserves essential switching functions independent of the host switch.

With diverse facilities connecting these modules to their host switching office, as well as to other offices, protection is provided for any single failure in the loop plant or the host office. The degree of protection can be engineered according to the customer's willingness to pay. It ranges from partial capability during an outage to full protection for all business-critical lines.

An excellent way to provide the loop-transmission diversity that large customers require is with fiber optic transmission and the Business Remote Terminal. Optical fiber service and protection channels can be installed in separate cables in physically diverse routes. If there is a cut in the service cable, the system automatically switches to the protection route in about 50 milliseconds, minimizing the effect on the customer. Through telemetry channels, the system tells the proper telecommunication operations systems to start the repair process. The telecommunication company also has the option to install the technical capability to provide status information to the customer.

Customers are also asking for network management capabilities to be provided by the public network. They want status and alarm information sent from the network, and control capability sent to the network. The Netpartner network management system, for example, has both capabilities, which include alarm surveillance, testing, traffic information, trouble ticket entry, station rearrangements, and route selection control.

(7) Facility Protection Services

New technologies are continually being developed to reduce the chance of fires and to limit the effect of those that do occur. These technologies include thermographic inspections to detect excess heat in equipment, the use of new materials to more effectively seal openings between CO floors and rooms, computer-aided matching of power cables to power requirements, and safer fusing. AT&T's facility protection services are offered to operating companies to inspect, rehabilitate, and maintain their building, prepare for emergencies, and reduce the risk of service disruptions.

(8) Rapid Deployment Service

The widespread use of very large scale integration (VLSI) devices and optical fiber have reduced the size of equipment to the point where all parts of the current generation of telecommunication equipment can be rapidly shipped by trailer. In an emergency, transmission terminals, power systems, distributing frames, or even a complete 5ESS switch can be sent within one or two days to any location in the United States. With pre-planning of equipment layouts, connectorized cables, *et cetera,* the switch can be operational soon after delivery.

After a local switching office is hit by a disaster, most of the time devoted to restoring operations is not for replacing the hardware, it is for building and loading the office database with information about the features associated with all the line and trunk terminations. To meet the increased expectations of customers, in the future, current backup copies of these databases may need to be stored in a secure location to speed the restoration process even further.

Another advantage of optical fiber technology is the reduced repair time after an outage. While a cut cable or equipment malfunction affects many more channels (because of the high bandwidth of optical fiber systems), an optical fiber cable is much easier to splice than a multipair copper cable of the same capacity.

(9) Today's Trials . . . Tomorrow's Developments

AT&T is currently meeting the rising expectations of today's customers for assured telecommunication service in several ways. The available technology already has significant automatic restoration capability. Networks can be engineered to the degree of reliability that is economically justified or called for by public policy.

In the last year, South Central Bell conducted a successful trial in Mississippi of AT&T's FT Series G lightwave system with a ring diversity switch. At the end of 1989, additional features on the FT Series G system included restoration access, single-ended maintenance, and unprotected operation for improved flexibility and robustness.

This year New York Telephone, with its pioneering Sentinel Showcase project, will be the first user of the DACScan-2000 Network Controller. While both DACS III-2000 and DACS IV-2000 are useful network elements in their own right, AT&T's new computerized DACScan-2000 Network Controller will centralize and automate the management, administration, and operation of broadband networks.

When development is complete, the DACScan-2000 Network Controller will automate the provisioning of circuits through DACS III-2000, DACS IV-2000, and other vendor's digital cross-connect systems. The controller will automate service recovery when there are transmission facility failures. When service is interrupted, the DACScan-2000 controller will display the failed connection and will provide its unique identification at the bottom of the workstation screen. It will also display the recovery plan, which may be generated in advance and stored in its database, or through algorithms using the current state of the network. The operator will be able to implement the plan or alter it by selecting a new route from available alternatives.

The DACScan-2000 controller automatically issues commands to the DACS systems in the network to change the cross-connections to reroute circuits and to implement the recovery plan. When repairs on the failed link are completed, the DACScan-2000 controller reinstates the original service plan.

During 1989, the Bell regional holding companies made several proposals to their customers for using the 5ESS remote switching modules on or near the customer's premises to provide dual access to the public network for more robust network access.

AT&T's engineering and installation services are being used by all regional holding companies to reduce network vulnerability and to provide a more protected environment in many COs. Simple inspections and preventive measures are viewed as a cost-effective means of improving the network's reliability.

A potential change in the future will be the use of non-hierarchical network routing techniques in the local public switched networks. Such techniques are used today in AT&T's long-distance network, where they greatly enhance network reliability in the face of traffic overload outages in individual nodes or links. The predominant hierarchical EO–tandem architecture will probably be modified to allow more switches to play the role of tandems. The increased deployment of Signaling System 7 (CCS7) in local networks will offer more robust routing capabilities. In the future, restoration features will improve toward the day when public telecommunication networks will be fully self-healing.

Acknowledgment

Our thanks to the authors:

Gerd W. Printz is an assistant manager in the Marketing Division, Network Systems, at AT&T in Holmdel, NJ.

Kathleen C. Szelag is a department head in the Transport Planning Department at AT&T Bell Laboratories in Holmdel, NJ.

Chapter 10
Protecting the Corporation—Everyone's Responsibility

This chapter was prepared by the law firm of Bickerstaff, Heath and Smiley of Austin, Texas, and is designed to be an overview of the legal issues that surround contingency planning. We would like to thank the authors, Katie Bond and Carolyn E. Shellman, for their hard work in preparing this handy overview for technical service managers.

10.1 TELECOMMUNICATION DISASTERS: LIABILITY ISSUES*

In the previous chapters the author has discussed various practical reasons why firms should engage in disaster recovery planning. This chapter focuses on one additional practical reason that could have very expensive consequences—liability.

The United States has become increasingly dependent on computer systems and the telecommunication network. For many firms, transmission of information over the telecommunication network is an integral part of their business. If a firm's communication service is interrupted and it cannot process and transmit information, even for a short period of time, the firm may lose the ability to transact any business at all. This disruption in service, of course, could mean that the firm will suffer substantial losses and could also mean that its customers or clients will also suffer financial injury.

---

*This chapter is contributed curtesy of Bickerstaff, Heath and Smiley of Austin, Texas. The authors address legal liability issues for corporations, public common carriers, and the government in protecting against disaster.

When a firm uses the telecommunication network as an integral part of its business and a disaster occurs, many questions arise: If the entity is a good corporation, what is the corporation's duty to ensure continued operation of its system? Can it be held liable to clients or customers who suffer losses if it did not take the steps it should have taken? What is the duty of the corporate officer in charge of managing the network to ensure continued operation of the system? Can this officer be held liable if he does not take adequate steps? Can the officer be held liable in a lawsuit brought by shareholders? If the entity is a state agency or political subdivision, can it be held liable? Can the telephone company be held liable either to its customers or to third parties if its actions or failure to act cause the disaster?

The purpose of this chapter is to provide a general discussion of these issues and give examples of how they could be resolved in certain situations. This discussion of legal issues is general and is not intended to address specific factual situations. The applicable law may vary from state to state, and the application of the law to the facts will vary with each different situation. Therefore, the reader is urged to consult an attorney for legal advice regarding applicable law and the legal ramifications of a specific situation.

(1) Liability of Private Firms

As discussed above, many firms depend heavily on computers and communication to provide services to their customers or clients. When a firm's telecommunication service is interrupted, the firm may not be able to provide its usual services. Depending on the nature of the business, its customers may suffer financial losses themselves as a result of the outage. If the firm is not able to recover its communication capability quickly, customers who have suffered losses might attempt to recover some or all of their losses from that firm. Liability could be imposed on a private entity such as a corporation under statutes and under the common law, which is the body of law made up of court decisions.

One kind of action that could be brought under the common law is an action for negligence. In a negligence lawsuit, a plaintiff generally must establish that the defendant had a duty to act in a certain manner and violated that duty. Whether a defendant has a duty is established by examining the risk, foreseeability, and likelihood of injury, weighed against the social utility of the actor's conduct and the magnitude of the burden of guarding against the injury.

The degree of care that a defendant is required to observe in the performance of a common law duty is the care that would be exercised by a "reasonable and prudent person" in the same or similar circumstances. In the context of telecommunication disaster planning, the issue might be, for example, whether a firm whose business is dependent on computers and communication had acted reasonably in taking the steps it did to assure quick telecommunication recovery (or whether it was reasonable not to have taken certain other steps).

Under the common law, a corporation's directors and officers can also be held liable for negligence. Generally, directors and officers owe a duty to exercise due care in the management of the corporation's affairs. This duty is owed to the corporation, and it can be asserted by the corporation or by someone acting on its behalf, such as a trustee in bankruptcy, a receiver, or a shareholder in a shareholder derivative action. (Note that this duty is not generally owed to a client or customer of the corporation.)

Like the "reasonable and prudent person" issue involved when a corporation itself is sued for negligence, the issue when a director or officer is sued is: What course of action would have been followed by a reasonable and prudent person in a similar situation? In deciding the answer to this question, the court would consider such factors as the condition of the corporation's business and accepted practices within the industry. An officer or director who is found negligent could be liable for any loss the corporation suffered as a result of the negligence.

As mentioned earlier, a corporation may be liable under statutory as well as common law for failing to take adequate steps to assure continued ability to operate. For example, under the Foreign Corrupt Practices Act, 15 U.S.C. 878m(b)(2) (FCPA), publicly held corporations are required to comply with certain record keeping and accounting control requirements. The FCPA was enacted by Congress as an amendment to the Securities and Exchange Act of 1934. One of the major purposes of the act was to require corporate disclosure of assets as a deterrent to foreign bribes. Another important portion of the FCPA is the accounting control provision, which gives the Securities and Exchange Commission (SEC) authority over the financial management of publicly held corporations. These requirements are relevant to disaster planning because many companies' accounting systems depend heavily on the use of computers and telecommunication systems.

Section 13(b)(2) of the FCPA requires public corporations to (1) make and keep accurate and reasonably detailed books, records, and accounts, and (2) maintain a system of internal accounting controls sufficient to provide reasonable assurances that, among other things, the assets of the company are adequately controlled.

The FCPA defines "reasonable detail" and "reasonable assurances" as the level of detail and degree of assurance that would satisfy prudent officials in the conduct of their own affairs. Several lower federal courts have held that the FCPA does not give a plaintiff the right to file a private lawsuit for damages. However, the SEC may enforce the act by holding a hearing on an alleged violation and requiring the corporation to comply.

A person may be criminally liable under the accounting controls requirements of the FCPA by knowingly circumventing or failing to implement a system of internal accounting controls. Other statutes or regulations applicable to a particular industry may impose a special duty or liability on firms in the industry. For example, the banking industry is subject to Banking Circular 177, which deals with contingency planning for electronic data processing support. Additionally, the corporation statutes may impose certain duties on corporations and their officers and directors. Generally, the law of the state of incorporation determines issues relating to the internal affairs of a corporation. These statutes should be examined to determine whether they impose a duty.

(2) Liability of Public Entities

Today, governmental entities are as dependent on computer systems and the communication network as private firms. Like private firms, many governmental entities perform services using computers and the telecommunication network. They provide such diverse services as tracking of hurricanes, transmission of information about criminals, and distribution of unemployment checks.

Just as private firms may be sued by customers or clients who suffer losses in a telecommunication disaster, governmental entities might also be sued in the event of a disaster and inability of the entity to recover quickly. Unlike private firms, however, public entities may be able to avoid liability to a significant extent because of long-standing policies regarding governmental liability that have become part of the statutory and common law in many states.

The principle of sovereign immunity means that the State cannot be sued unless it consents to being sued. In other words, the State must have "waived" sovereign immunity before it can be sued. Furthermore, the State can be sued only to the extent it has consented to be sued, i.e., only under the conditions established in the waiver of immunity. This principle applies both to the State and its agencies and to political subdivisions of the State, such as cities and counties. The federal government and states have enacted statutes that allow persons to sue the government under certain situations. If a situation does not fit within the statutory waiver of sovereign immunity, then the governmental entity is immune from suit.

For example, the Texas tort claims act provides that the State of Texas, its agencies, and it political subdivisions may be sued for property damage, personal injury, or death caused by the negligence of an employee acting within the scope of his employment if the damage, injury, or death arises from (1) the operation of a motor vehicle or equipment, or (2) a condition or use of personal or real property. Statutory waivers of sovereign immunity often limit the amount of damages that can be recovered in addition to circumstances in which liability can be imposed. For example, the Texas statute limits money damages for property damage to $100,000 per occurrence.

Special rules may apply to cities. Whether a city is liable could depend on the type of service that the city is performing. The law often distinguishes between whether a city is performing a "governmental" function and whether it is performing a "proprietary" function. Governmental functions are functions such as fire, police, tax collection, and water and sewer service, while the operation of public utilities and amusements are often called proprietary functions by the courts. If a service or function is governmental by nature, then the city will generally be liable only to the extent specified in the statutory waiver of sovereign immunity. To the extent a city is performing a proprietary function, it will be liable for the negligence of its employees.

(3) Liability of the Telecommunication Carrier

Recent events highlight the vulnerability of the U.S. telecommunication network. The Hinsdale fire in May 1988 disrupted the telecommunication service of thousands of customers, some for several weeks. The January 1990 switching failure of AT&T lasted only nine hours but resulted in a nationwide network outage. These service disruptions affected many people and conceivably had a devastating impact on some firms.

A firm whose service is disrupted by a telecommunication disaster may consider suing the telephone company or the long-distance carrier on the basis that there was some error or omission in the way the company provided service. For example, in the Hinsdale case, customers may have sued Illinois Bell for negligence, raising the question of whether Illinois Bell took adequate fire and security measures.

Customers who sue the telephone company or long-distance carrier will find, however, that the tariffs approved for these companies by either the FCC or state regulatory commissions may limit the companies' liability significantly. Consequently, injured customers may find it difficult to recover their losses. The limitation of liability in Southwestern Bell Telephone Company's Texas tariff is typical of the limitations contained in the telephone company tariffs:

> The Telephone Company's liability, if any, for its gross negligence or willful misconduct is not limited by this Tariff. With respect to any other claim or suit, by a customer or any others, for damages arriving out of mistakes, omissions, interruptions, delays or errors, or defects in transmission occurring in the course of furnishing service hereunder, the Telephone Company's liability, if any, shall not exceed an amount equivalent to the proportionate charge to the customer for the period of service during which such mistake, omission, interruption, delay, error, or defect in transmission or service occurs and continues. (Southwestern Bell, Texas General Exchange Tariff, Section 23, Sheet 9, para. 8.7.)

Under this provision, if a customer sues the telephone company and tries to establish that it was negligent under the "reasonable and prudent person" standard, the telephone company would probably prevail and its liability would be limited. Thus, the customer who had substantial damages would be limited to recovering from the telephone company the *pro rata* charge for the period of time during which its service was interrupted.

The above tariff provision does not totally limit the telephone company's liability. It states that the telephone company's liability for gross negligence or willful misconduct is not limited by the tariff. This statement reflects rulings by the courts that it is against public policy for a telephone company to try to limit its liability in those situations, as opposed to situations involving ordinary negligence. The legal definition of "gross negligence" varies from state to state, but generally the term means that a person has exhibited conscious indifference to the rights or welfare of others. The term "willful misconduct" generally means the intentional doing of something with the knowledge that it is likely to result in serious injury.

Since both gross negligence and willful misconduct require a showing about a person's state of mind, they are much more difficult to establish in a lawsuit than ordinary negligence. Generally, if a person simply makes a mistake or commits an error, he or she will not be held liable for gross negligence or willful misconduct. Courts have generally ruled that limitations of liability similar to the one found in Southwestern Bell's tariff are reasonable. However, there are isolated cases in which a court has found that a limitation of liability was unreasonable.

Courts have also ruled that it is reasonable for these provisions to limit the company's liability to third persons who were damaged because the customer's service was interrupted. Unless a customer or third party can establish that the telephone company was guilty of gross negligence or willful misconduct or has a compelling argument why the limitation of liability for ordinary negligence is unreasonable in a given situation, then the telephone company's limitation of liability will apply.

(4) Limitations of Liability, Insurance, and Indemnification

One way that a firm can attempt to protect itself from liability resulting from a disaster is to include limitations of liability in the contracts it has with its customers or clients. These may not limit the firm's liability in all situations but would provide protection under some circumstances.

A firm may also be able to obtain insurance to cover loss or liability in the event of a telecommunication disaster. A general liability policy would probably cover liability for personal injury or property damage. An errors-and-omissions policy might cover liability for economic losses resulting from negligent actions or failure to act, such as failing to plan properly for disaster recovery.

Business interruption insurance may also be available to reimburse a firm for certain amounts if its system goes down and it is unable to function for a specified period of time. When investigating the type of insurance coverage available, you should examine carefully what coverage is included and what is excluded from a given policy. For example, some errors-and-omissions policies may cover directors and officers but exclude employees.

A corporation could also investigate the possibility of indemnifying its directors and officers. The extent of a firm's ability to indemnify these persons depends on the law of the state of incorporation. Additionally, indemnification may not be available in some matters involving the SEC. Indemnification statutes often differentiate between actions by or on behalf of the corporation and actions by third persons, and the extent of indemnification allowed varies according to the type of action. Depending on the state's law, a corporation may be allowed to indemnify its directors and officers for expenses of defending lawsuits, amounts paid in settlement, and judgments. To the extent that a corporation indemnifies its directors and officers, it may want to obtain insurance that insures against this risk.

(5) What Should You Do?

Several steps can be taken to limit or reduce possible liability and loss in the event of a telecommunication disaster.

1. Work with your communication manager to identify the types of problems that could be caused for your clients or customers if your system failed.
2. Identify the vulnerabilities in your network and, to the extent possible, develop backup programs or build in redundancies (if they are not cost prohibitive).
3. Review customer contracts and consider inserting limitation of liability language in them.
4. Develop a disaster plan that addresses, for example, the following issues: persons with responsibility; contracting with alternative providers of service; whether on-site generators could be used to restore power to your system if external sources failed; use of multiple sites for processing or transmitting critical data.
5. Purchase insurance.

If a disaster occurs, your firm may not avoid all loss or liability, but if these steps are taken, you will be able to show that you acted reasonably and prudently. From the perspective of reducing legal liability, the more anticipation and planning you can demonstrate, the more likely it is that your reactions to a disaster, despite how well they work, will be considered reasonable. Additionally, careful planning can reduce the amount of loss suffered by your business itself in a disaster.

Chapter 11
Epilogue

Throughout this book the need for a viable telecommunication disaster recovery plan for corporations has been stressed repeatedly. The most notable reason for the planning effort, the possibility of legal liability in a disaster, has been covered extensively. This potential threat is real and should not be ignored. There is a second good reason, however, for a cohesive planning effort. For lack of a better term, we will call it the "human factor."

The most important reason for corporations to have the foresight to plan ahead is people. In a large service-oriented corporation, thousands of people and their families derive their income and livelihood from the company. Performance of their jobs is often wholly dependent on the services you provide them. Most of these individuals think of the phone as nothing more than a business tool. They know nothing of data communication circuits, which link their offices to distant computers in other cities. A network planner, however, should always remember that a single data circuit could support an entire branch office—and the jobs of a dozen or more people.

A telecommunication disaster could be much worse in specific industries, not only to employees, but to those outside the company who depend on its services. Benefit check disbursement for the unemployed, retirees, welfare recipients, indigent persons, and dozens of other classifications has become highly automated. In most cases, the return to manual processing would be virtually impossible. Even if it were possible, the delay for many of these people, who often live from paycheck to paycheck, could devastate entire families. In other cases, loss of law enforcement computers could mean that fewer felons would be caught since there would be no electronic means of tracking their activities.

Another example is the area of emergency services. The continuity of civil emergency services is of paramount importance. Federal, state, and local emergency management planners must take the initiative to ensure that adequate communication systems will exist after a major disaster, such as a hurricane. If they do not, the resulting lack of command and control needed for coordinating emergency response would again mean needless human suffering after a calamity.

These are just a few of the many reasons why contingency planning is important. Disasters hurt people who are dependent on the company. Contingency planners have a moral responsibility to their users. In the course of planning recovery capabilities for these complicated systems, we must never lose sight of the forest for the trees, and we must always remember the real reason for disaster planning: *People depend on your service.* The responsibility for protecting this service is yours.

Chapter 12
Glossary

10XXX dialing. 10XXX represents the unique five-digit access code assigned to each common carrier in the United States. Customers in EAEOs can access any carrier that purchases access into that particular LATA by dialing 1, 0, and the unique three-digit number assigned to the carrier selected, hence the term 10XXX.

Access Tandem. The primary serving office for a given LATA through which much of the common carrier access is derived. Some types of access links like Feature Group "B" are provided almost exclusively from the Access Tandem. Others such as Feature Group "D" may be derived from the Access Tandem or an EAEO.

"Backhoe fade". Slang term, common among telecommunication professionals, meaning "cable cut."

Cell site. A cellular radio transmitter that provides mobile telephone service to a particular area of town. Mobile telephone users have their calls switched from cell to cell as they drive from one part of town to another, otherwise known as a "hand-off" between cell sites.

BOC. Bell Operating Company.

CO. Central Office.

DACS. Digital Access Cross-Connect System. Commonly used in COs for cross-connecting circuits. DACS units can connect T1s, individual circuits, or elaborate combinations of the two, as well as T3 connections. This equipment is gradually replacing manual (soldered) connections in many COs.

Demark. Common telephone company term for the telephone company's network interface installed at the customer location. Telephone company responsibility starts and stops at this location; wiring inside the demark location is the responsibility of the customer.

Digital hub. Designated CO that provides maintenance, circuit timing, and other advanced functions for digital data circuits. While many offices now provide digital services, in many cases "premium" digital service is routed through this specialized office.

Divestiture. This term refers to the 1984 breakup of AT&T into AT&T Communications, AT&T Bell Laboratories, and AT&T Technologies, as well as the seven regional Bell telephone companies such as NYNEX and Bell South.

DS-1. Another term for T1, or T-carrier; a 1.544 MB circuit.

DS-3. Another term for a T3 carrier; a 45 MB circuit.

EAEO. Equal Access End Office. *See* End Office.

End Office. The type of CO that provides local exchange services directly to end-users, instead of to other COs. Also called the Local Serving Office. It was classified as a "Class 5" office prior to the 1984 divestiture, and is now classified as an "Equal Access" or "Non-Conforming" End Office depending on its configuration.

Feature Groups A, B, C, and D. Special access lines to the local exchange leased by long-distance carriers to provide LATA-wide origination and termination of long-distance traffic. Feature Group D is accessed from the Access Tandem or an EAEO. It allows for 10XXX, 1+, or 0+ dialing to the designated carrier. Feature Group B is provided almost exclusively from the Equal Access Tandem switch. It allows for access via the 950-XXXX dialing plan to allow use by subscribers in NCEOs. Feature Group C is currently available only to AT&T.

Fiber optic loops. Refers to redundant paths built into fiber optic cable routes to divert traffic automatically or manually in the event of failure of the primary path.

Halon fire systems. Commonly used in computer rooms, Halon is an odorless gas that is discharged quickly into a room to extinguish a fire by cutting off oxygen, while still leaving enough to allow for respiration of the room's occupants. It is generally considered harmless to humans, although it is expensive and sometimes subject to accidental discharge.

Hitless switching. Refers to a technology applied to many communication mediums (microwave, fiber, *et cetera*) to provide a very fast "switch" to a backup facility in the event of failure on a primary path. This happens quickly enough to assure that the facility does not drop calls already in progress, or disrupt data, hence the term "hitless."

Hot site. A backup computer facility that provides standby (idle) mainframes of a given type for use in the event of a disaster in a corporate computer center. These facilities are available on a "members only" basis for which subscribers pay a per month retainer fee for the right to utilize the computers in the event of a disaster in their facility.

Inter-LATA. Refers to circuits that originate in one LATA, but terminate in a different LATA. These circuits are carried by AT&T or another long-distance company.

Intra-LATA. Refers to circuits that originate and terminate in the LATA, which is serviced by the local (Bell or GTE) operating company.

ISDN. Integrated Services Digital Network. An advanced digital service offering designed as an industry standard to provide much greater capacity and more advanced features than standard telephone service.

LATA. Local access transport area.

Local access cable. The cable facility from the Local Serving Office to the end-user. The last link of a circuit to the user.

Local Serving Office. The serving office from which the user draws regular dial telephone services. It is also the last CO utilized before a circuit is connected to an end-user.

M24/M44 multiplexer. Term that denotes a CO D4-compatible T1 multiplexer that conforms to AT&T's M24 or M44 standard. The M24 multiplexers combine twenty-four 64 kb channels into a single T1, and M44 multiplexers use ADPCM multiplexing to derive forty-four 32 kb channels from a T1 circuit.

Metropolitan area network. Any non-Bell network within a metropolitan area that has the purpose of providing local exchange services similar to those offered by the BOCs. Sometimes called "alternate access" carriers.

NCEO. Non-Conforming End Office. Class of CO that is not capable of providing equal access to carriers other than AT&T. *See also* End Office.

NXX codes. An NXX code is the first three digits after an area code in a telephone number; it identifies the CO to which the number is assigned. By using the area code and NXX code (such as 617-223-XXXX), COs anywhere in North America can be readily identified.

OCC. Other common carrier (other than AT&T). Term common in the pre-divestiture era and still used today.

POP. Point of presence. A POP is a meeting place where local exchange facilities connect to long-distance companies. Hence, the terms, AT&T POP, MCI POP, *et cetera*.

Private line circuit. Also called a "special" or "custom" circuit; it could be voice or data. Private line circuits provide any service other than normal dial tone service.

Regional Toll Office. Another term for the primary Bell or AT&T office that served a large metropolitan area or geographic region prior to divestiture.

Right-of-way. The public utility easement through which public services such as water, sewer, telephone, cable television, electricity, and other services are routed. Many times rights-of-way are also controlled by railroads, utility companies, highway and transportation departments, pipeline companies, and others. A right-of-way is an important factor when installing communication facilities.

Robust network. A term finding increasing use, particularly among BOCs and AT&T. It describes a network with fault-tolerant systems designed to be resistant to accidental service disruptions.

RS-232. A 25-pin computer-to-modem connector.

Shell site. A backup computer facility that provides raised floors, special power, and other computer infrastructures for use in a disaster. Unlike a "hot site," computers are not provided. Instead, the customer arranges for quick delivery from manufacturers, using the shell site as a place to set up and rebuild.

Special facility construction. Broad term given to any type of unique, custom services constructed by the BOCs specifically for a large customer.

T1. A 1.544 MB circuit that provides twenty-four 64 kb channels.

T-carrier. Term commonly used within the BOCs for T1 circuits installed between Bell serving offices.

Toll Center. Name given to the primary Bell serving office in the pre-divestiture era. Usually contained such items as the Bell testboard and operator services center.

Toll Point. Same as a toll center, but with no operators.

Transponder. A single "channel" on a satellite. There are 24 transponders on each satellite.

Tropospheric scatter system. Radio communication system used by the military. The system sends an extremely high power signal in the direction of the horizon. While most of the signal continues into space, enough of it is reflected by the atmosphere to allow a receiver (located many miles over the horizon) to receive the transmission. It is commonly used overseas in desolate areas where other facilities do not exist.

The Author

Leo A. Wrobel holds degrees in Telecommunications Systems Technology, Electronics Systems Technology, and Business and Public Policy. He held various positions with AT&T before moving to Lomas Information Systems as Manager of Network Planning and Engineering. In 1986, Mr. Wrobel founded Premiere Network Services Inc, a Dallas consulting and telecommunications disaster recovery firm where he is President and C.E.O. He is also consulted in matters of telephone regulation, and is a City Councilman. Professional affiliations include membership in the IEEE, DPMA, and Association of Contingency Planners.

Specific enquiries or questions to the author can be directed care of Premiere Network Services Inc, 17304 N. Preston Rd. Suite 800 Dallas, Texas 75252 (214) 733–6870.

The Artech House Telecommunication Library

Vinton G. Cerf, *Series Editor*

Advances in Computer Systems Security: 3 volume set, Rein Turn, ed.

Advances in Fiber Optics Communications, Henry F. Taylor, ed.

Broadband LAN Technology by Gary Y. Kim

Codes for Error Control and Synchronization by Djimitri Wiggert

Communication Satellites in the Geostationary Orbit by Donald M. Jansky and Michel C. Jeruchim

Current Advances in LANs, MANs, and ISDN, B.G. Kim, ed.

Design and Prospects for the ISDN by G. DICENET

Digital Cellular Radio by George Calhoun

Digital Image Signal Processing by Friedrich Wahl

Digital Signal Processing by Murat Kunt

E-Mail by Stephen A. Caswell

Expert Systems Applications in Integrated Network Management, E.C. Ericson, L.T. Ericson, and D. Minoli, eds.

Handbook of Satellite Telecommunications and Broadcasting, L. Ya. Kantor, ed.

Innovation in Internetworking, Craig Partridge, ed.

Integrated Services Digital Networks by Anthony M. Rutkowski

International Telecommunications Management by Bruce R. Elbert

Introduction to Satellite Communication by Bruce R. Elbert

Introduction to Telecommunication Electronics by A.Michael Noll

Introduction to Telephones and Telephone Systems by A. Michael Noll

Jitter in Digital Transmission Systems by Patrick R. Trischitta and Eve L. Varma

Manager's Guide to CENTREX by John R. Abrahams

Mathematical Methods of Information Transmission by K. Arbenz and J.C. Martin

Measurement of Optical Fibers and Devices by G. Cancellieri and U. Ravaioli